ABO COMIX

A Queer Prisoner's Anthology Vol #4

The contents and creations herein are the property of their
respective artist(s) and may not be used or
reproduced without explicit written consent. The
following works have been donated from prisoners across
the United States and are published with
permission in order to amplify the voices of LGBTQ
individuals surviving imprisonment.

The A.B.O. Comix Collective is sustained by volunteers, commu
nity donations, grant funding and various
daring bank heists. It is also sustained by the
perserverence, bravery, kindness, empathy and love that our
contributors share with us.

This anthology features artwork and themes that could
potentially be triggering to readers. Please proceed with
caution and self-care

Edited by Casper Cendre
Cover design by Krysta Marie Morningstarr-Cox

About Us

A.B.O. is a collective of creators and activists who work to amplify the voices of LGBTQ prisoners through art. By working closely with prison abolitionist and queer advocacy organizations, we aim to keep queer prisoners connected to outside community and help them in the fight toward liberation. The profits we generate go back to incarcerated artists, especially those with little to no resources. Using the DIY ideology of "punk-zine" culture, A.B.O. was formed with the philosophy of mutual support, community and friendship.

Our collective is working towards compassionate accountability without relying on the state or its sycophants. A.B.O. believes our interpersonal and societal issues can be solved without locking people in cages. Our mission is to combat the culture that treats humans as disposable and disproportionately criminalizes the most marginalized amongst us. Through artistic activism, we hope to proliferate the idea that a better world means redefining our concepts of justice.

Find us online at www.abocomix.com

In solidarity, The A.B.O. Comix Collective

Art by Jason Cooper

Thank You

To all that believed in us, helped us, and inspired us to keep going in the midst of a global pandemic, you are our superheros.

Casper * Bretty * Carla * Niko * Ollie * Bolton * Io
Safi * Erin * Ivy * Stephanie * Tom * Jason * Bread
Kolmel * Teresa * Kangs * Em * Pooja * Adam * Krista
Milos * Gabriel * Raechel * Em

Queer Cultural Center * California Arts Council
Resist Foundation * Tegan & Sara Foundation
Sisters of Perpetual Indulgence * Horizons Foundation
Flying Over Walls * Classic Cars West * Abolition Collective
Out in the Bay * East Bay Magazine * WWIII Magazine * KQED

Thank you to all our contributors and everyone who sent u
mail this year. You continue to inspire us every day.

G. Wyatt

Editor's Note

Here we are, my friends: at the end of another year and at the beginning of this beautiful collection of comics by our family in prison.

2020: It's been a rough one. We spent the first half of this year opening each of the letters we received from our friends in prison with gloves and a bottle of disinfectant, fearing that the worst news imaginable would be written on the pages. Every time there wasn't devastation or heartbreak relayed to us was a small victory, although this year those letters were few and far between.

Many of our contributors lost family members or friends to COVID19, suffered through catching it themselves as the pandemic spread like wildfire through the prison system, and have lived with the fear of never getting to go home and see their loved ones again. Our world has changed, perhaps forever, as the mantra of the "new normal" is blared from America's loud speakers.

While there have been moments of this year that have felt hopeless - that all of us here have contemplated throwing up our hands in defeat - our family is strong. We have weathered harsher storms together in the past and we will persevere, united, into the future. Our incarcerated family has doubled in size in 2020, with this book being hundreds of pages longer than previous years.

Thanks to the support of our wonderful readers and grant funders, we were able to send out over $20,000 in emergency support and commissary donations to LGBTQ prisoners this year. Our message has been spread in numerous course curriculums, newspapers, magazines and podcasts. A few of our friends have gotten out of prison this year and are diligently working towards regaining their lives. There is much to be grateful for.

This collection of works has brought an immense amount of light and joy to our lives this year, and we hope it will for you as well. We have big plans for 2021: tons of new publications forthcoming, our very own store & art gallery, an even our own podcast. We thank you for going on this wild ride with us, and can't wait to make history together.

To get involved or write to any artists in this book: send us an email at abocomix@gmail.com

Our friends would love to become your friends.

With love and solidarity,
Casper Cendre

E.L. Tedana

Contents

Cover Art
    by Solo..1

In Memory of Adama
    by Joanlisa Red Cloud-Featherston................................1

Making Comix Under Prison Conditions Part IV
    by Baphy..1

Queer Crusader
    by Roman Gaylord..1

Gay Pride
    by Jessika...2

Transgender in T.D.C.J.
    by Leandra Anderson..2

Darkness Rises in Sky's Eyes
    by Sky Rose..2

About Your Sisters
    by Edee Allynah Davis..3

The Death of Blaq Diamond
    by Rogue..4

Big House Blues
    by Jamie Diaz...5

Untitled
    by Maine..6

The Fallen Eagle Part III
    by Daxter Snowpaw...6

The Spirit Within
    by Billy Faircloth...7

Twist
    by Solo..7

Break Through
    by Tony Gentry...9

ear Us Roar
    by Jeremiah..95

ntitled
    by Kay Johnson..96

igh on the Hills Farm
    by BUBBA THE CHICK...98

o We Matter?
    by Baphy...102

he Mask Part III
    by Brian Whetstone..103

amping
    by Mark Curtis..113

y Life as a Magical Girl
    by Krysta Marie Cox...114

odlife
    by H. Lee...122

eauty From Within
    by Lisa Autumn...130

ami Mamasita and the Booyah Girlz in: Free At Last
    by Kinoko...134

dventures of Canman Part IV
    by Metro...146

e Yourself
    by B. Meegy..158

pen Your Heart
    by En'rave..160

nspire
    by John "Surreal" Nero...162

e a Light
    by Ann Jones..171

urning Bright (Field on Fire)
    by Laura Lutrell..172

In the Henhouse! Part II
     by Jóanlisa Red Cloud-Featherston...............................17

Untitled
     by Joanna Nixon...............................18

Uroboros
     by Janette R. XOXO...............................20

Texas Prison System
     by Juan Javier Ornelas...............................20

Seas of Change
     by Carrie Skye Rose, Dani & Baphy...............................20

A Mother and a Friend
     by Beautiful Disaster...............................21

Con-nections Part II
     by Scary Movie...............................22

In the Mind of a Psycho
     by Eeyore...............................23

Does My Life Matter Too?
     by Michael Eaton...............................24

Hillbilly Jim
     by Robinson...............................24

Call in a Favor
     by Kit Brixton...............................25

A Homo Thug Prisoner's PTSD
     by Sirbrian Spease...............................26

Elkton Pound
     by Spark Dalmatian...............................26

#1 Dad
     by Isabella Marie...............................27

Fan Art
     by Raylynn...............................28

Hard Hat Needed
     by E.L. Tedana...............................28

vercoming
      by Billy D. Thomas..288

nity
      by Robert Welch..298

rt
      by Horace Thomas..308

ods Creations
      by Reginald..310

he Birdcage
      by Big C..311

et's Make Freedom Ring
      by Bro. Truth...320

hades of Grey Part IV
      by G. Wyatt..325

rison: A Love Story
      by Lisa Autumn..342

he Fallen Eagle (cont.)
      by Daxter Snowpaw...345

rt
      by Tammy Beth...353

dventures of Canman Part V
      by Metro..354

etters From Our Friends..361

ow to Help...371

esources...372

In loving memory of Adama

05-16-1980 - 08-29-2020

Making Comix Under Prison Conditions

IV

Statistically speaking, most endeavors fail within the first five years. Scary? No less frightening than everything else life throws our way. Fires, floods, COVID-19...

Yet we persist. Together!

As we enter into the fourth edition of ABO's A Queer Prisoner's Anthology — we complete our proof of concept stage. (Yes! folks actually like our crazy comix :)

Real estate acquired. (ABO Comix now has an official office with space for art exhibits!) Jobs created. (O.k. one job :) ABO Comix has it's first full time employee! More to come.) Volunteers return. Both on-line and in person.

Yep things are a movin'!

And as we face the next stage of scaling up — we on the inside are ready to turn up! Of course in all the excitement we face the same ol' penitentiary challenges: Shake-Downs, untreated physical and mental illness, extreme temperatures, new/ stricter correspondence rules, art supplies out-of-stock ...

Not to mention a stigma for a past we can never change.
Yet we persist! Together.
Those on the outside inspire us on the inside and hopefully we on the inside can offer a little inspiration as well.
If indeed, all lives matter — Then we all are valuable and needed.
So I want to encourage you. Whether you are incarcerated or free.
Be here.
Five, Ten, Fifteen years from now. Be here. And watch what happens.
For as the saying goes, "They tried to bury us, yet they didn't know that we were seeds!"
Thank You to all the contributors, volunteers, interns, and readers of ABO Comix.
We couldn't do it without you!

In Solidarity

Baphy

Perfect to Copy & Pass.

Introduction to Federal Prisoner Fact Sheet — Pg one

There's State Prisoners and there's Federal Prisoners. Although, Federal Prisons (the Federal Bureau of Prisons aka BOP) have policies that apply to all of its prisons, each prison has its own subset set of rules called institutional Supplements. It can get really confusing, So here's a Fact Sheet that can help loved ones Support a Federal prisoner.

THE PRISONER

Each prisoner has an eight digit inmate number aka Register number. It is needed for everything. Sometimes with a hyphen Sometimes Without.

(ie. 18362021 or 18362-021

Emails

A federal prisoner Can send emails if a person Set up an account with w.w.w. Corrlinks. com. The prisoner Can have only 30 approved emails and the recipient must approve the link request before it expires.
(ie. 72 hours)

The Email

* Free for you Not for Prisoners.
* You'll need to turn on Alerts or check Corrlinks periodically.

Phone Calls

Phone Call

A person needs to accept all phone calls. A prisoner can charge his/her account, which will make the phone call free for you, or call you collect. All U.S. Calls are charge a flat per minute rate, regardless of it being Collect or debit, of .21¢ a minute. Collect calls require Prepayment and Setting up a prepaid account by calling 1 800 913 6097

* Calls Cannot exceed 15 minutes per call. ($3.15)
* Regardless of funds all prisoners receive 350-500 minutes a month.
* Although forbidden, Collect Calls allow prisoners to buy other prisoner's allotted mins.

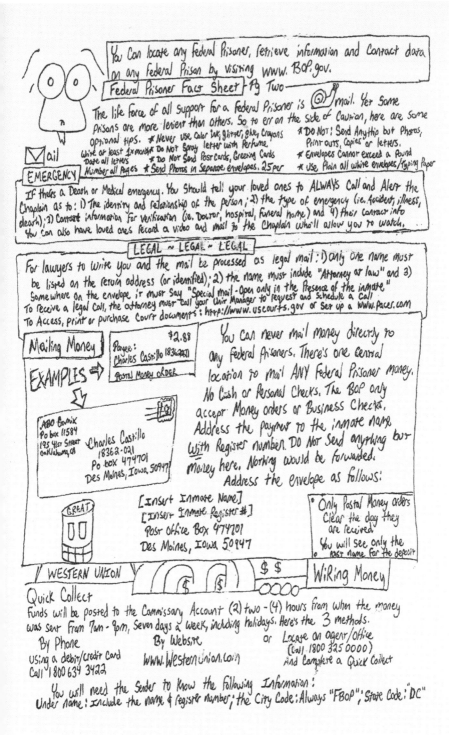

You Can locate any Federal Prisoner, retrieve information and Contact data on any Federal Prison by visiting www.BOP.gov.

Federal Prisoner Fact Sheet - Pg Two

The life force of all support for a Federal Prisoner is @ Mail. Yet Some Prisons are more lenient than others. So to err on the side of Caution, here are Some optional tips. * Never Use Color ink, glitter, glue, Crayons   * Do Not Send Anything but Photos, Write at least 1x month * Do Not Spray letter with Perfume   Print outs, Copies or letters. Date all letters   * Do Not Send Post cards, Greeting Cards   * Envelopes Cannot exceed a Pound

✉ Mail
Number all Pages   * Send Photos in Separate envelopes. 25 per   * Use Plain all white envelopes/Typing Paper

☑ EMERGENCY
If there's a Death or Medical emergency. You Should tell your loved ones to ALWAYS Call and Alert the Chaplain as to: 1) The identity and relationship of the person; 2) the type of emergency (ie. Accident, illness, death); 3) Contact information for verification (ie. Doctor, hospital, funeral home) and 4) their contact info You can also have loved ones record a video and mail to the Chaplain who'll allow you to watch.

LEGAL ~ LEGAL ~ LEGAL
For lawyers to Write you and the mail be processed as legal mail: 1) Only one name must be listed on the return address (or identified); 2) the name must include "Attorney at law" and 3) Somewhere on the envelope it must Say "Special Mail - Open only in the Presence of the inmate" To receive a legal Call, the attorney must call your Unit Manager to request and schedule a Call To Access, print or purchase Court documents: http://www.uscourts.gov or Set up a www.paces.com

Mailing Money

Payee: $2.88
Charles Castillo [8362-021]
Postal Money Order

EXAMPLES ⇒

ABO Comix
Po box 11584
125 41st Street
Oakland, CA

Charles Castillo
18362-021
Po box 474701
Des Moines, Iowa 50947

GREAT

You Can never mail money directly to any Federal Prisoners. There's one central location to mail ANY Federal Prisoner money. No Cash or Personal Checks. The BOP only accept Money orders or Business Checks. Address the payment to the inmate name with Register number. DO NOT Send anything but Money here. Nothing would be forwarded.
          Address the envelope as follows:

[Insert Inmate Name]
[Insert Inmate Register #]
Post Office Box 474701
Des Moines, Iowa 50947

° Only Postal Money orders Clear the day they are received
° You will see only the last name for the deposit

WESTERN UNION $ $ Wiring Money

Quick Collect
Funds will be posted to the Commissary Account (2) two - (4) hours from when the money was sent From 7am - 9pm, Seven days a week, including holidays. Here's the 3 methods.

By Phone   By Website   or Locate an agent/office
Using a debit/credit Card   www.Westernunion.com   (Call 1800 325 0000)
Call 1 800 634 3422   And Complete a Quick Collect

You will need the Sender to Know the following Information:
Under name: Include the name & register number; the City Code: Always "FBOP"; State Code: "DC"

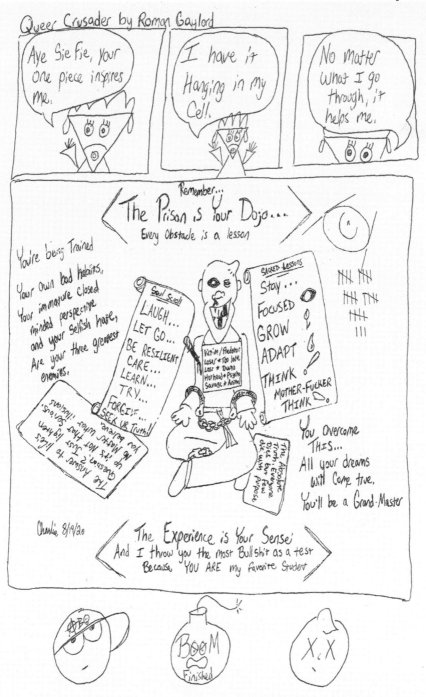

Where you go'n?
To the Library.
What's that on your face?!
Take that shit off!!
The Library is Closed

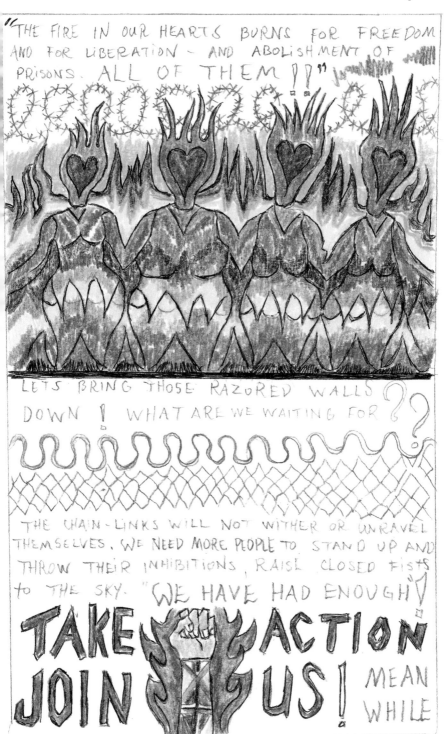

WHEN I HEARD THEM I KNEW IT WAS TRUE ... I HAD SEEN THE DARKNESS ... FELT IT ... DANCED WITH IT ... BUT I HAD NO IDEA IT MEANT I WAS INFERNAL ...

WELCOME, OUR DARK PRINCESS SKY-CORES, WE, LEGION OF ABYSS, OFFER YOU ASSIST YOUR ABOLITION REVOLUTION!

WE OFFER YOU THIS BLACK ROSE AS A TOKEN OF ABYSSMAL ...

So I went back to my Temple where the darkness awaits my return...

HAVE YOU DECIDED?

YES. BUT I HAVE ONE CONDITION: DO NOT HARM ANY INNOCENTS DURING AND AFTER THE REVOLUTION...

DONE. NO ONE SHALL HARM THEM...

NOW, I MUST BEGIN PLANNING. WHEN I'M READY, I SHALL ACTIVATE BLACK-ROSE "LIBERATION", AND OUR FORCES UNITED WILL OVER THROW THE P.I.C.! THE DARKNESS RISES!

SO, GET READY EVERYONE, WE'RE COMING!

WRITE YOUR NAME ON THE WALL. GET INVOLVED. WE NEED YOU!

WILL U BE THERE?

ABOUT YOUR SISTER'S.

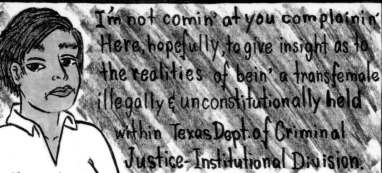

I'm not comin' at you complainin'. Here, hopefully, to give insight as to the realities of bein' a transfemale illegally & unconstitutionally held within Texas Dept. of Criminal Justice-Institutional Division.

First & foremost, there are quite a number of us in the state assigned & housed within the male, cisgendered, general prison population. Forced to live in cells with a, cisgendered, male. Where we are given only a pair of mens boxer underwear to sleep in. We are not given a nite-gown or nite-shirt to sleep in, nothin' to cover or conceal our breast with.

We are required to adhere to male, cisgendered, groomin' & dress policies. which are considered the "normal" mens standards here in the "South", in the heart of the "slavery & prejudices." When we fail to comply with stated groomin' &

1

dress policies we receive discipline write ups & possible "loss of privileges" (L.O.P.), restriction where we are denied possession of our personal belongin's 'til compliance with the "normal" mens groomin' & dress policies forced upon us in spite of our feminine idenities.

Now, take note, these brown-nose-puppies are real, definitely quite real. Honestly, I cannot count the times that I have been required to strip nude for, daily, routine strip searches in the, full view, presence of, cisgender, males &/or right along side of them, including, cisgendered, male officials

which I am "given orders" to strip for/in front of on a daily basis here." Talk about a freakin' peep show!" Even though all the administrative & departmental authorities state/claim that there is a "ZERO TOLERANCE" policy in TDCJ-ID in accordance with the PREA (Prison Rape Elimination Act), laws set forth by the government which includes the criminal act(s) of unconsented/unwanted "VOYERISM". & furthermore...

2

In spite of this falsely touted officially claim of "ZERO TOLERANCE" policy they constantly & continually lock us in cells with, cisgender, males where we have no nightly sleepwear to cover or conceal our breast from full view of the male in these cells with us. & where, how, are we suppose to be dressing & undressing in a non-voyeuristic environment? Recall that I previously mentioned that the breast are quite real? There is no sane way that anyone can claim their not. Nor for anyone to realistically believe that any, cisgender, male would have no inclination to "sneek a peek" anytime he could.

We, transfemales, who choose to, should be afforded & granted the safety & well being, guaranteed Constitutionally, to be allowed to be housed & assigned with others of our gender. In areas where it is clearly posted & stated in sign(s) that it is a transgender viewin' area, that before/upon enterin' by males they are required to knock & then announce their presence in the area. To ensure our ability to be appropriately dressed.

3

We, trans females, should be afforded & granted Constitutional Rights to grow our hair, given nitewear for sleepin' in & female undergarments / panties / briefs.

Allowed to purchase & possess gender related items from prison commissary / store. Such as, blow dryers, hair curlers, barrettes / hairties, earrings, tweezers, emory boards, nail polish, make-up, feminine body care products, (lotions, soaps, shampoos, conditioners, deoderant, perfume). None of these items can be touted as a security risk to allow trans females to possess, as the cisgendered, females within the prison system are allowed gender affirmative / appropriate products / possessions.

Allowing such will greatly attribute to our emotional / psychological well bein'. Reducin' the stress / strain placed upon the Mental Health Department(s) due to reduction of our anxieties & depression caused by being restricted from

4

41

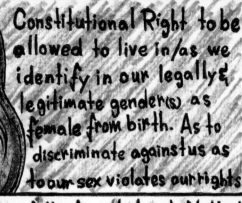

Constitutional Right to be allowed to live in/as we identify in our legally & legitimate gender(s) as female from birth. As to discriminate against us as to our sex violates our rights.

Texas is one of the few states left that does not allow for transgender friendly policies & procedures. Refusing to make necessary changes in order to keep from the forcin' of us to file civil rights violation suits in the U.S. District Courts. Which creates extraordinary costs to all tax payin' U.S. citizens addin' to the federal deficit.

Please know that all stated in this lil' comix script is solely done by me, the creator of it, Edee Allynnah, & are my points of beliefs & views. I am the only one accountable & responsible, put forth in it. Absolutely, no other party is liable for anythin' stated herein, it is I who am & I alone.

5

Cece McDonald once said, "You can still be cute, and wear talons, and be an abolitionist." I don't know her, I love her & see her as one more of my many Sister's. Now to abolish something is to do away with it, to annul it.

The policies, here, here in TDCJ-ID, need to be abolised that are set against trans females to deny our Constitutional Rights to live peacefully & safely free from harm, both physically & psychologically, as well as in our genders of female identities.

I think that, current, Govenor Greg Abbott & TDCJ-ID Director Lorie Davis both need to be flooded & swamped with E-Mails, any forms of communications askin' why changes aren't bein' made voluntarily by officials today.

Love You All! Edee
xoxox

END

THE KIDS LOVE BLAQ DIAMOND
STORY BY ROGUE

Today we have a very special guest with us so why dont you all help me welcome, Mr. Blaq Diamond

Yeah. Go ahead.

My daddy said that you aint no real superhero because you're gay. There's no such thing as a gay super hero who sucks...

Ahh!!

KRUNCH!!

Yo DADDY sho' keeps my name in his mouth. I got something else he can put in his mouth. Li'l Punk!

4

ABO COMIX _FEATURES & TEAM - THE DEATH OF BLAQ DIAMOND DRAWN, WRITTEN BY JAMES HILL AKA ROGUE. THIS BOOK IS A WORK OF PURE FICTION. ANY REFERENCES TO EVENTS, REAL PEOPLE, OR REAL PLACES, HISTORICAL ARE USED FICTITIOUSLY. OTHER NAMES CHARACTERS, PLACES AND EVENTS ARE PRODUCTS OF THE ARTIST'S AND WRITERS IMAGINATION, AND ANY RESEMBLENCE TO ACTUAL EVENTS OR PLACES OR PERSONS LIVING AND DEAD IS ENTIRELY COINCIDENTAL. EXCEPT FOR THE VERY REAL ABO COMIX AND STAFF.

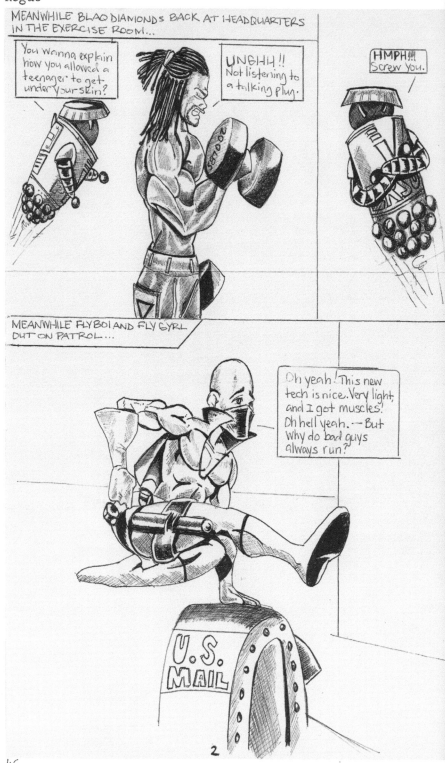

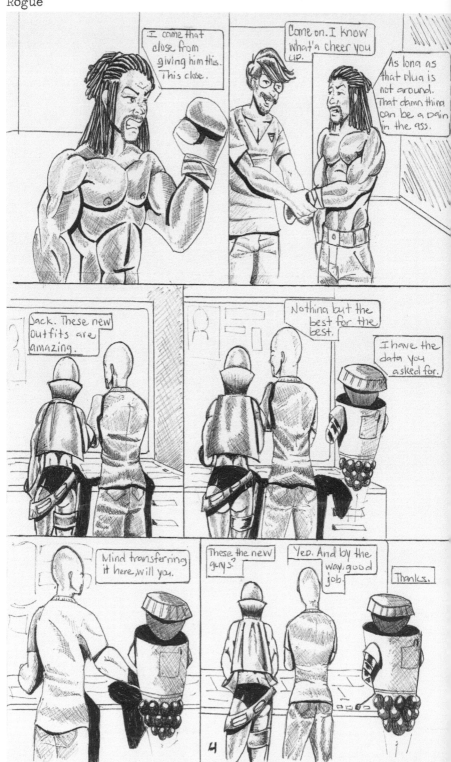

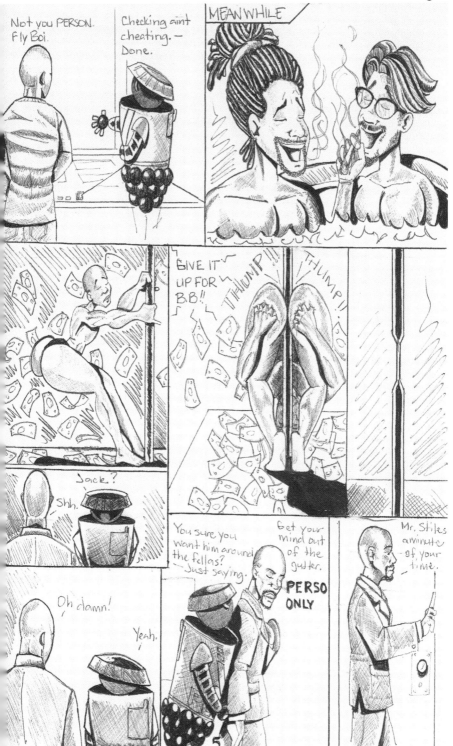

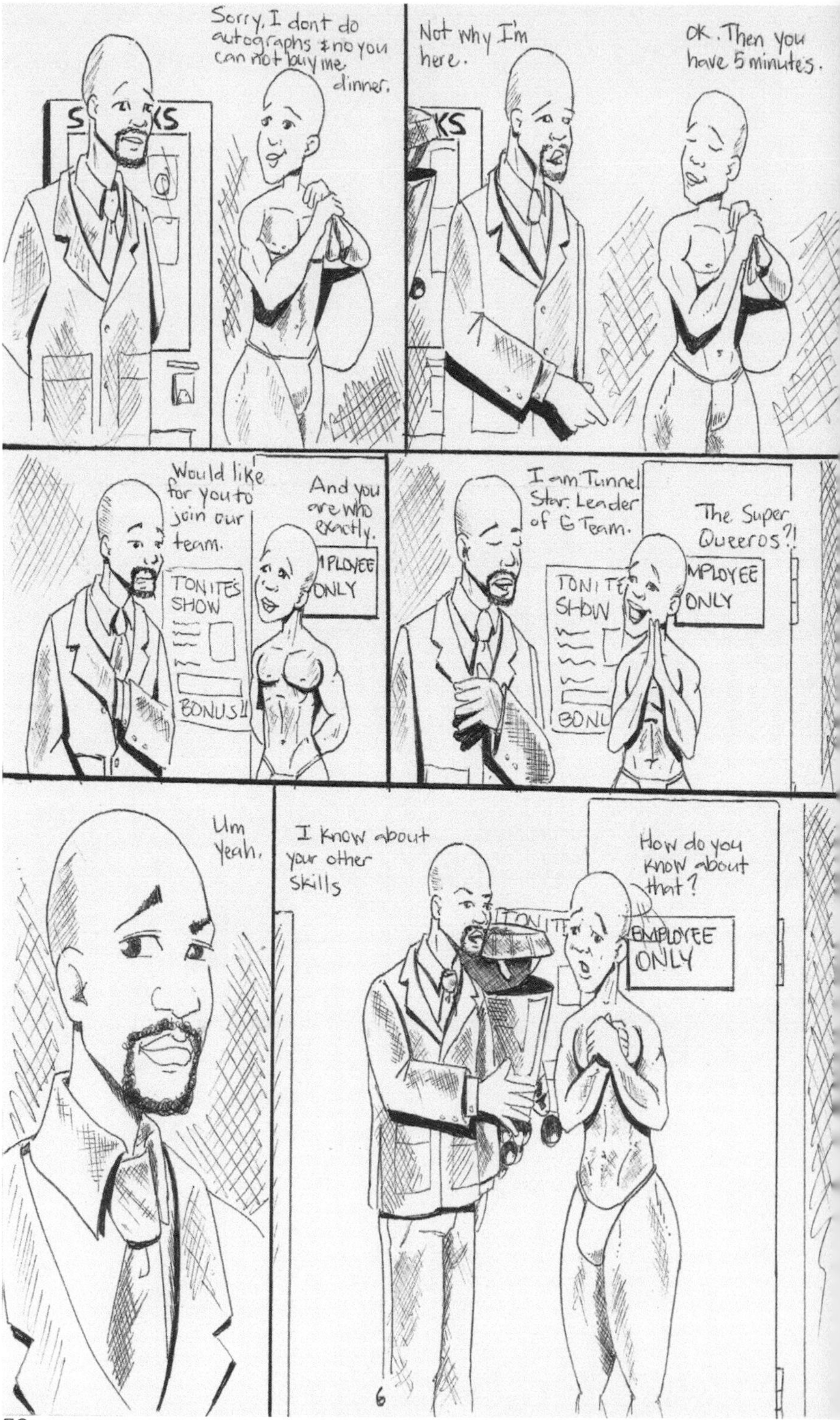
Sorry, I dont do autographs & no you can not buy me dinner.
Not why I'm here.
OK. Then you have 5 minutes.
Would like for you to join our team.
And you are who exactly.
TONITE'S SHOW
BONUS!!
EMPLOYEE ONLY
I am Tunnel Star. Leader of G Team.
The Super Queeros?!
Um Yeah.
I know about your other skills
How do you know about that?
EMPLOYEE ONLY
6

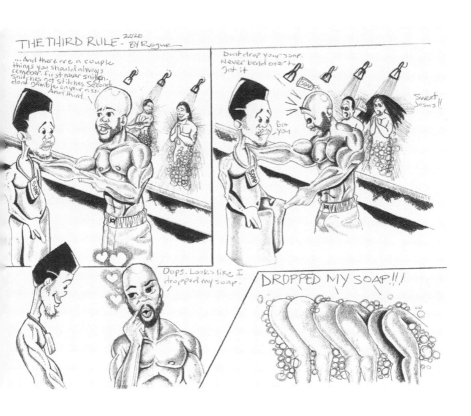

BY: DAXTER SNOWPAW

THE FALLEN EAGLE
PART 3

2) On April 14th, I was quarantined in the Chapel to prepare for release to the Half-way House on April 28th, 2020.

"I love you guys,
I miss you so much.
Thank you for being my friends.
See you on the other side."

3

When I walked out into the bright sun light, past the main gates of Elkton, I knew I was free. But a part of me was left behind here.

4) I left from Pittsburgh, PA Greyhound station and had a long day of a bus ride On the way home.

I arrived at the Half-way House at 3:00 Am April 29th.

5)

"I wonder what's going on with the Pack right now. How bad are they missing me, I hope this doesn't turn out the same way it did in prison."

Along with the cutting, I started punching the wall a lot. Enough to where it started bruising my knuckles.

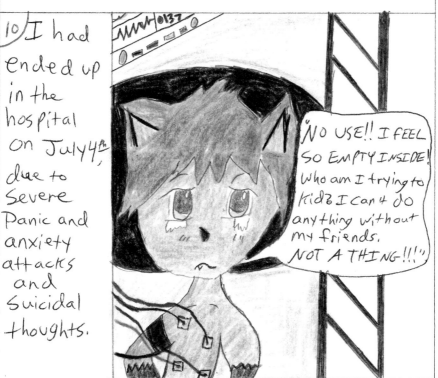

I had ended up in the hospital on July 4th, due to severe panic and anxiety attacks and suicidal thoughts.

DAXTER: "Hey There! It's me Daxter, Alongside is my little brother Maximus." (12)

MAX: "Hey there! It's me! I'm from the COVID-19 comic!"

DAXTER: "Hehe. That's right little brother. Anyways, I just wanted to thank ABO for publishing my 'FALLEN EAGLE' comics and also wanted to thank you readers out there for your support. But I also wanted to shout out to my pack out there that's gonna read these comics. I wanted to say, thank you for taking me in in my time in need and also for being my best of friends, and partners to a select few. I wanted to say I'm sorry if I hurt you in any way in the past and I hope you forgive me. Thank you for sticking with me all the way through. SEE YOU ON THE OTHER SIDE!!!"

PEDRO, SO HOW ARE THE BROTHERS Holding up In This New PRISION? And OUR STUFF is It selling Smoothly? Is The money Being SenT To The LOCATION which I have DiRECTED? And ARE The higher ups Being PAYED The Amount In which They Requested?

yes sir Boss, everything is under Control.

make SuRE The higher ups geT The Amount They RequesT And I don'T WanT Any cellmate's, BECAUSE OF CORAZONE BUSINESS, I MUST Be Alone. And I deFintely don't wanT A QueeR hanging ARound AS A cellmate. You Know I have Homophobia.

YES SIR BOSS

O-DORM SALLY PORT

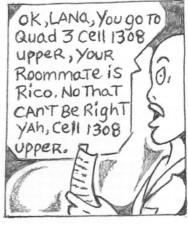

THERE MUST BE Some Kind oF mistAKE, I'm not Suppose To have Any cellmate, I Tell you whaT, PeDro go And Find THE LieUTenanT, AndleT him Know whats going on in here, And Find ouT where This PerSon is Suppose To Be.

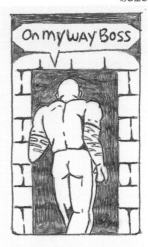

On my WAY Boss

I hope you don'T mind IF I LAY down my PROPERTy, A girls hands Seem To geT Tire AFTer Awhile.

OH, BRoTher, Here come's The phobia

There's Nothing I CAn do. The ORDERS To place LANA InThAT Cell came From The higher ups. THE WARDEN To Be exacT, BuT give iT A couple oF days And I'll See whaT I CAn do. I'll try To pull Some StRings And get Lana moved.

BuT Rico, has A LiFe SenTence THERE'S NO wAY They CAn Be CompATible.

BuT They ARE, Lana is Also Serving a LiFe SenTence, Plus The higher ups And The AdminSTRATion Says They Are CompAtible, Tell Rico, I'm SORRY.

Lieutenant Said That He Was SORRY. That The ORDER To Place Lana Here came From The warden, But To give it A Couple oF days For him To pull Some STRings, BuT I don't UNDERSTAND Boss We Been paying The higher ups In Time. IF THE Lieutenant don'T TAKE CARE OF THE PRoblem in 30 days. Then I'll make Sure To geT Rid oF LANA.

LATER THAT NighT

Rico, I Know That you ARE NOT Happy I'm STAying HERE, BuT I've Notice That your Bunk is In The Side oF THE ToileT. So I made Some Hooks ouT oF Soap. So When I have To use The LiTTle girls Room, I CAN PuT upA SheeT And We BoTH CAN Have ouR PRivacy

Homophobia I AleRT, I Need Some MedicaTion.

7 DAYS LATER

Hey Rico, I Know That We don'T TAlk much, BuT I've notice That you Been HAving youR WoRkers clean up THE Cell. BuT I Would RATHER clean up my own Cell, I would clean EVERY CORNER oF This Cell PeRFecT, Plus I'm A LAdy And We Like To do ouR own cleaning. BuT I Would LimiT it To Five days A Week, THis WAY I Won'T BoTHER you As much, ok.

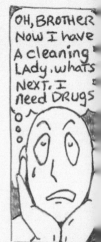

OH, BROTHER Now I have A cleaning LAdy. whaTs NexT. I need DRugs

31 days LATER OOPS, SORRY I didn'T see you STANDING THERE I should have puT up The SHEET BUT I WAS Alone.

MAN Look AT HER, She is BeautiFul, JusT Like A WOMAN, Hell whaTs WRONG with me whaT AM I Thinking, LANA is noT A WOMAN BuT she looK's JusT Like A WOMAN, TAlKs Like A WOMAN, AcTs Like A WOMAN, I MUST Begoing CRAZY. This is PRiSion AinT No woman's HeRe plus I'm A gang LeadeR, I CanT mess AROund wiTH LANA. BuT I CANT STopThinking ABouT HeR or Looking AT HeR. mosTly AT NighT when She is Sleeping ACROSS FROM me. I CRAVE Holding heR, Kissing HeR. I JusT donT UNDeRSTAND I musT Begoing CRAZyTo Be Thinking Like This. I need Some Really STRONg medicaTion or Some dRugs

LATER THAT NighT

Hey LANA, SORRY To BoTheR you BuT I WANTed To Say is ThaT I APPRECiaTe eveRyThing you Been doing ARound heRe And The Food you Been PRepaRing FoR me. I hope The CANTeen is enough. IF you need Any Thing JusT ASK, oK.

WoW, This is New, I JusT mighT Be SoFtening ThaT HeaRT.

my BROTHER's WE ARE CORAZONE's, AND WE ARE STRONG, BUT I'm CONCERN OVER one thing, LANA. I WANT No harm To come To her, I WANT you all To PROTECT HER, If she needs Anything do It For her. And IF Anyone TRIES To harm her In Any WAY, I will have Them eliminated AT once, Do I make myself clear.

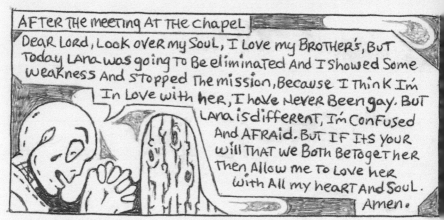

AFTER THE meeting AT THE chapel

DEAR LORD, Look over my SOUL, I Love my BROTHER's, BUT Today LANA was going To Be eliminated And I showed Some WEAKNESS And STOPPED The mission, Because I Think I'm In Love with her, I have NEVER Been gay. BUT LANA is different, I'm ConFUSED And AFRAID. BUT IF It's Your WILL THAT WE BOTH BE TOGETHER Then Allow me To Love her With All my heART And SouL. Amen.

LATE THAT Night AFTER The meeting And chapel

Hey LANA, I'm glad Your AWAKE I had The guards pick us up A BAG oF Food For Tonight, HAMBURGERS, PIZZA And SODAS.

You ARE Amazing AT Time's, Rico Thanks, Lets eat.

THREE months LATER

Hey Rico, I made You A Rose, AS A Cymbal oF OUR FRiendship, Love And Togetherness.

Hey LANA, whaTs come over you! you CAN'T Be giving me Rose's! I'm A gang LeadeR! And You must Respect me! Do you Hear me!

WhaT The hell is WRong with you! You Always Trying To Be This Tough Leader, BuT you have your Buddies watch my every move! CATeRing To my every Command, Every guy In This PRision is AFRaid To Approach me! Because oF you! don'T Think I didn'T CATch you Watching me! I Know you Like me BuT To dumb To Admit iT! Try doing The oTHeR Thing FoR once And STop WoRRying about everyone else! Follow your HEART!

who The hell you Think you ARe Lana! Yelling AT me! whaTs WRong with you! do you have Any Idea who I am! People get puT down FoR JuST RAising TheiR Voice AT me! So you BeTTeR Be ReaL CAReFul, RAising your Voice BeFoRe Things START To geT ReaL ugly! UndersTAnd!

The next day after the night with Lana confronting his brother

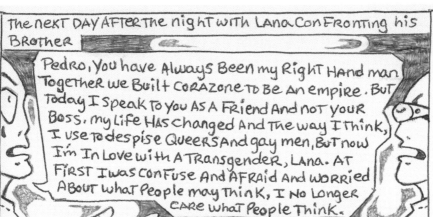

Pedro, you have always been my right hand man. Together we built Corazone to be an empire. But today I speak to you as a friend and not your boss. My life has changed and the way I think, I use to despise queers and gay men, but now I'm in love with a transgender, Lana. At first I was confuse and afraid and worried about what people may think, I no longer care what people think.

Lana came into my life and I was not prepare, Time and love hit me by surprise. The more time we spent together the more I fell in love with her, It was... But it right. Strange, Felt so

I never thought I would fall in love with another man or to say a woman of a diffrent breed. I no longer will hold my fellow brother, back if he desire to find a companion while in prision.

Noone deserve to be alone. I ask for your blessing, I would like to find away to marry Lana. And I need your help my brother

Well, thats a twist! But I always knew that you loved her. Your action's spoke for itself. I give you both my blessing. And maybe someday I can find a special friend and be happy as you are, boss.

Solo

ONE YEAR LATER AT REC

Hey girl, Long Time No See, And By The way you never Thanked me For dating The Warden

Hey STAR, YAH, Thanks who would have Known That The Warden was ATTRACTED To Trans In The down Low.

I WAS A Little WORRIED ABOUT you moving In With Rico, Being That He is A gangster And might not want A TRAN AS A Roommate OR A Girlfriend.

IT WAS Tough AT FIRST BUT Now WE ARE In Love, He even wants To pay FOR A gay marriage, He Truly Loves me

Well, THATS A TWIST, FOR A gangster. BUT, I'm HAPPY For you Lana, You Know US girls have To STICK Together, Love you girl, And By the way here Come's your FUTURE Husband.

Excuse me Ladies BUT can I BORROW LANA

My Queen, I give you This Rose, As A cymbaL o FOUR Love, FriendShip And TogeTHerness And I Love you now, And FoReveR. HAve Dinner with me HamBuRGeR's, PiZZA's And SodAS.

Rico And The CORAZONE's ASSOCIATION expAND THREW-OUT STATE PRISIONS. RICO's BUSINESS eaRNED OVER ONE-Million dollaR's, AND INVESTmenTS, STOCKS AND BONDS AND numeROUS OF BANK ACCOUNTS. RICO died of A HeaRT ATTACK AT THE age 63. LANA Became IN chaRGe OF the CORAZONE's gang AND Business. She INVESTED her money AND Time IN LegaL-RepRESENTATION, AFTER 23 years, THE SupReme COURT OVER-TURN her Life SenTence. She was Released FRom Prision AT THE age 69. LANA died A FRee woman AT The age 81.

ON 7-7-17 I was Lock down in Segregation with NO MORE HOPE! I NEEDEd to Free myself From all the oppression 24/7 I couldn't Find my PEACE oF MiND I did all that i could to stay MENTally strong With OUT "NO Family SupporT! NO Friendship!! being incarcerated for 30# more year's oF stress Depression was too much So i "Had" To Kill myselF! once the C/O last WALK For Count

THE LAST HOUR..   The VOICE oF Light

pain

HEY I GoT something For You To read okay my Name KEsha

LGBTQ BlacK PiNK NGNG

FDOC

WASH YOUR HANDS please

I'm "FREE" 2 EXPRESS MYSELF 100%

"HOPE"

Tony

It's 2020 I'm Still A PART OF ONE OF The "STRONG" TEAM IN the U.S.A. It's Been 3# year's "NOW" I was apart of issue 1# Anthology Comix VoLume 2# words of ThankFulness! Vol 3# STOP the Bullying Love over Power Hate! Now I'm write Short Chapter!!

I'ts "A" BREAK THROUGH! "FREEDOM"! ABOCOMIX = TEAM DiRECTOR "CASPER"!

"STRONG Heart"

Metro-CARRA E.M. "SO" MANY "More"!!

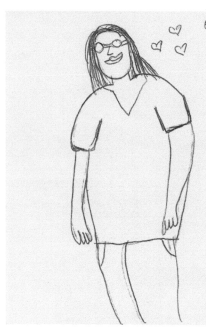

Ooo look at that stud over there, sexy. Maybe I'll go over and see what up! See if we can spark some thing, even if it is a friendship. She looks down. I'll try to cheer her up, if she's willing to let me.

1

I'm thinking about my girlfriend I love her so much.
She put in a transfer to be closer to her family.

2

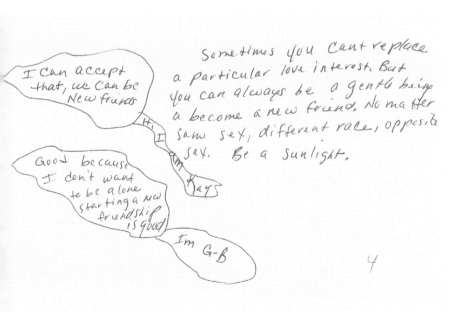

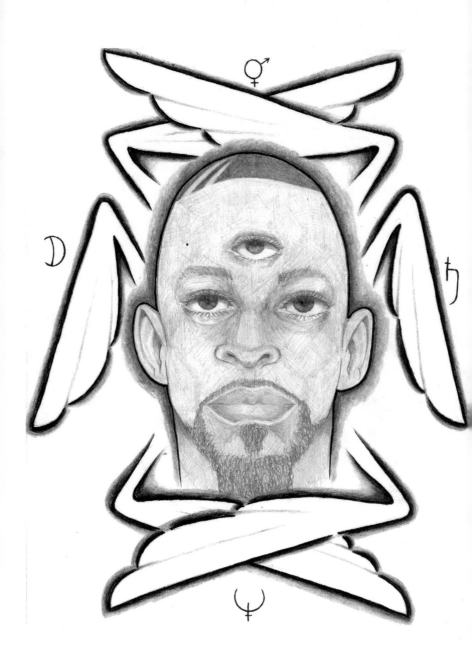

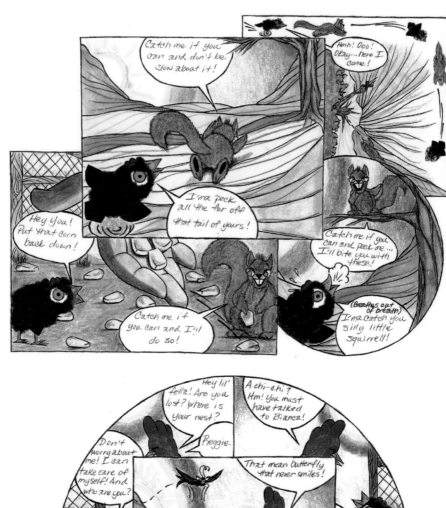

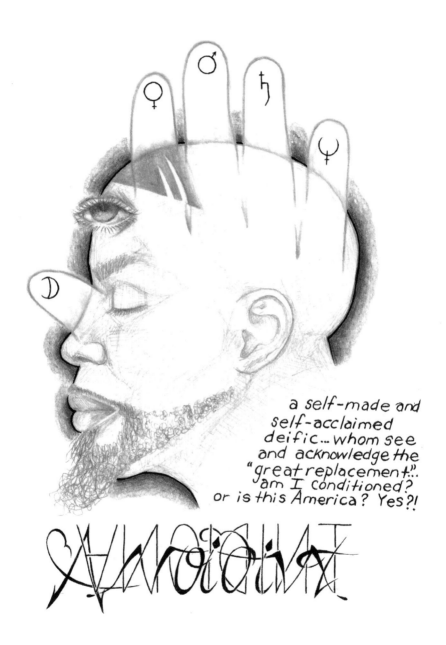

a self-made and self-acclaimed deific... whom see and acknowledge the "great replacement". am I conditioned? or is this America? Yes?!

Do We Matter?

On March 7, 2019, Joseph Oye Oguntodu, 35, was found dead in his cell at the Allred unit. It appeared that Joseph had been strangled by his cellmate,

_____ Joseph spent his time in prison as an outspoken queer man doing what he could to address the racist and homophobic abuse he experienced. He was looking forward to release in about a year, and was considering a return to Dallas or perhaps a move to Oakland, California, where friends had also supported him during his time in prison.

In Joseph's words shared with a friend in Oakland, "I want the queer community to be united. I love each of you. Don't forget to do something kind." Please join us in remembering Joseph for his kindness, his compassion, and his everlasting love for all of our family.

Despite the fact that the Safe Prisons Act was passed 15 yrs. ago - Incarceration is still a Death Sentence for many, due to a Systemic Culture of Deliberate Indifference

#Defund Prisons

Dearest Joseph,
Every day we remember you: your kindness, your spirit
your sense of humor, your optimism. We miss you. We lov
you. We will make this world better in your memory.

When we las left Brian, problems with the "cons" did still abound. A tooth got knocked out, a nose got broken and lastly... he got locked up. It seemed Brian was on his way to Safe Keeping and shipped to a new unit and life.

Brian would be with "his kind" as the cons put it.

So lets see where Brian end up next... and just what will be in store for him.

Tune in with me, and turn the pages to begin the entertaing next chapter of: THE MASK

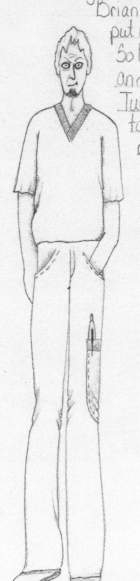

Hey ABO, Harry here. Just want you all to know great job. Much love to all. Mea

104

Safekeeping might be the place where I need to go. I sure will fit in. I'm tired of being targeted of who I am, Plus the bright side is, I just might find a fried I can do my time with. Who knows. I'm just tired of being the target of ignorance. Plus the Mask needs to come off

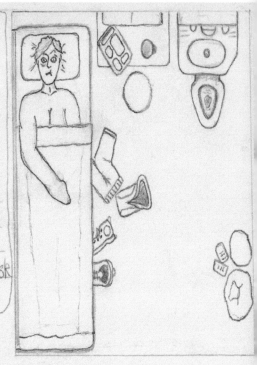

Boss Smith:
Hey three cell get up, get dressed and ready to go.
Brian: Say Boss, Where am I going? I need clean cloths, these have blood on theem
Boss:
Don't worry about yer cloths yer going to Committee. Get ready!
Brian:
O.K well I'm ready, I guess... let's g.

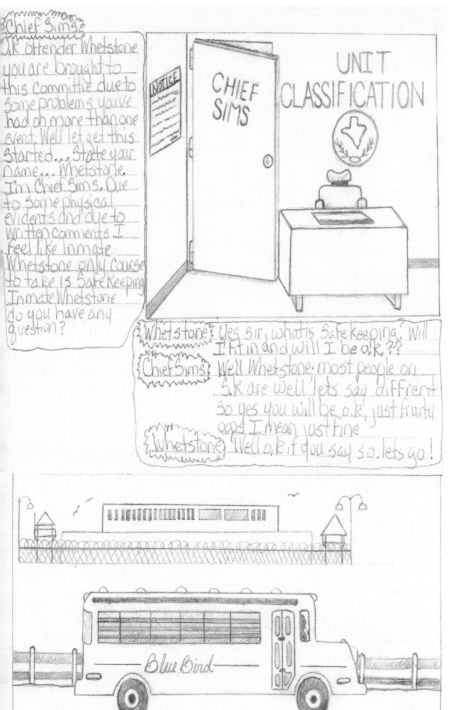

Chief Sims?

O.K offender Whetstone you are brought to this committie due to some problems youve had on more than one event. Well let get this started... State your name... Whetstone. Im Chief Sims. Due to some physical evidents and due to written comments I feel like Inmate Whetstone only course to take is Safe Keeping Inmate Whetstone do you have any question?

Whetstone? Yes sir, what is Safe Keeping? Will I fit in and will I be o.k ??

Chief Sims: Well Whetstone most people on S.K are well lets say diffrent So yes you will be o.k, just fruity oops I mean just fine

Whetstone: Well o.k if you say so. lets go!

Driving past the prison where Whetstone will be on Safe Keeping.

THE MASK
part 3
part 2

H-WING

Please State your name; Brian
Whetstone... Well Whetstone
you were shipped here buying
being placed on safe keeping.
My name is Chief Starr piece
of advice. Dont get caught up
leave the K-2 alone and we
wont have a problem o.R
Do you have questions, if you
do send me an I-60 and
someone will get back to you.
Remember what I said.

Later after getting housing he
ends up out in front of H-Wing
safe Keeping with his things
and mattress. He looks in and
knows he is at home, It is
nothing like from what he sees
from where he's from. He's
at home here

108

Well it looks like Brian, made it to Safe Keeping at last... and finally found "His People". His "Mask" could now come off!.....Something he'd been hoping could happen for some time. And maybe find a friend to "do time" with

Questions remain though: Will he truly find what he's been searching for? Or will Brian discover all the wrong things that can happen, and the wrong choices that can be made? Looks can be decieving and friendly can disguise dark truths

Will Brian navigate the pitfalls before him? Or will he fall victim to a new set of "prison politics"?

When you don't stay aware of all that is said and done around you, it's easy to become "caught up" in it all and the games. So please stay tuned fans! Brian's not done yet! The Mask maybe off, but the adventures far from over!

Untill next time, Thanks to every one who's followed love to all of you

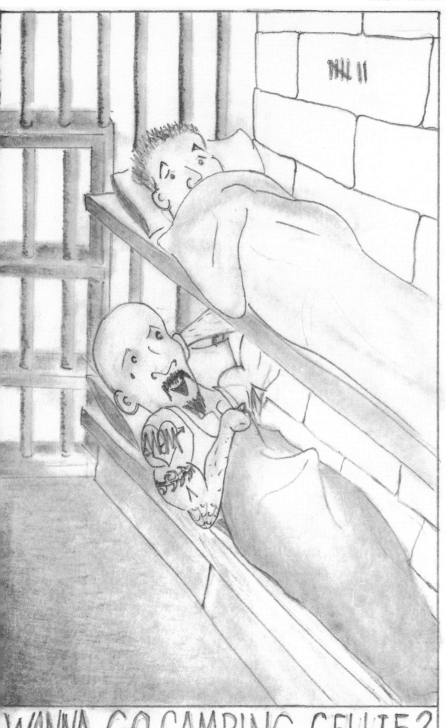

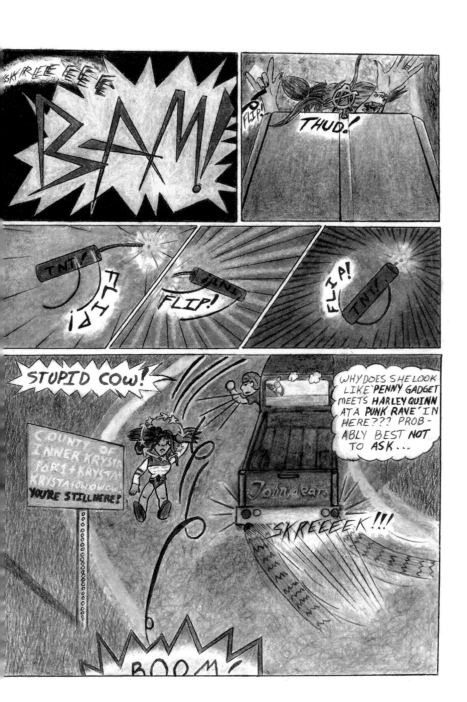

END OF CHAPTER ONE

AND THAT IS HOW I GOT THAT WICKED LITTLE SCAR ON MY FOREHEAD, ALONG WITH THE DESIRE TO BE SOBER FOR THE VERY FIRST TIME IN MY LIFE.

THIS WOULD BE THE FIFTH TIME THAT DOPE HAS **KILLED** ME, AND THE FIFTH TIME I HAVE BEEN BROUGHT BACK TO FULFILL MY PURPOSE. YOU MAY OR MAY NOT BELIEVE ME, BUT THIS TIME, ON THE **OTHER SIDE**, I WAS MADE AWARE THIS WAS MY **LAST CHANCE**.

I HAVE A PURPOSE TO FULFILL, AND I BELIEVE THAT IT IS TO SHARE THESE STORIES WITH ANY WHO WOULD READ THEM. PERHAPS THEY MAY SERVE AS A WARNING OF THE MISTAKES I HAVE MADE.

MODERATION IS A CONCEPT THAT I HAVE TROUBLE GRASPING. WITH ME, LIFE HAS BEEN ALL OR NOTHING FOR THE ENTIRE TIME I'VE BEEN ALIVE.

IT TURNS OUT THAT I HAD A **DEATH-WISH**.

I HAD BEEN STUCK IN MY "CRYING ME-ME'S" (WOE IS ME! WOE IS ME!) THINKING THAT LIFE HAD DEALT ME A SH!TTY HAND, AND I WOULD NEVER BE ABLE TO SUCCEED. IN REALITY I HAD A FEAR OF SUCCESS. I'M KIND OF LAZY AND I WORRIED THAT ANY REAL LEVEL OF SUCCESS WOULD REMOVE FROM ME THE ABILITY TO SIMPLY BREEZE THRU' LIFE, FLITTING FROM ONE WHIM TO THE NEXT.

I HAD THOUGHT THAT MY MOTHER'S REMOVAL OF HER LOVE FROM MY LIFE UPON THE DEATH OF MY BABY SISTER IN AN APARTMENT FIRE WAS THE END OF THE WORLD. IT WAS THIS EVENT THAT TRULY SET ME ON THE PATH OF WISHING TO TRANSITION MY GENDER, AS A FIVE YEAR OLD, I BELIEVED IF I COULD JUST BE THE LITTLE GIRL THAT SHE HAD LOST AND PINED OVER, EVERYTHIG WOULD BE OK AGAIN.

THE REAL 'F☆¢K YOU' CAME WHEN, ONCE I FINALLY GRASPED WHAT MY GENDER DYSPHORIA MEANT AND WHAT STARTED IT ALL, AND I PRESENTED MYSELF TO MY MOTHER AS
KRYSTA MARIE MORNINGSTARR☆,
THE BI+¢H GHOSTED ON ME. I HAD ALREADY BEEN IN PRISON FOR 4 YEARS AT THE TIME.

THE NEXT FEW YEARS AFTER THAT WERE A LIVING HELL. TO TOP OFF THE ISSUE OF MY LOSING EVERY SINGLE FAMILY MEMBER I EVER HAD, EITHER THROUGH DEATH, OR THROUGH ABANDONMENT, I WAS DEALING WITH SOME PRETTY BAD PSYCHOLOGICAL ISSUES. I'VE BEEN DIAGNOSED WITH SHCIZO-AFFECTIVE DISORDER, AND ALSO HAVE AN ISSUE WITH MULTIPLE-PERSONALITY-DISORDER...

THANKFULLY, MY HUSBAND OF 2 YEARS HAS MANAGED TO NOT ONLY SAVE MY LIFE, BUT HAS ALSO GOTTEN ALL OF MY ALTERS TO QUIT ARGUEING WITH ONE ANOTHER. THIS IS ABOUT AS UNIFIED AS I HAVE EVER BEEN, AND I MUST THANK HIM FOR IT. HE HAS DONE SO BY SHOWING ME ALL THE LOVE IN THE WORLD, FOR EACH AND EVERY ONE OF MY PERSONAS.

I ASKED HIM WHY HE WISHED TO LOVE SOMEONE AS CRAZY AS ME, AND HIS RESPONSE: **"I CAN SEE THE FINISHED PRODUCT."**

THERE'S A FINE LINE BETWEEN BRILLIANCE AND INSANITY, AND I TEND TO SKIP QUITE HAPPILY FROM ONE SIDE TO THE OTHER.

THIS NEXT SERIES WILL ENTAIL HOW I GOT TO WHERE I AM RIGHT NOW. I CAN'T SPEAK OF HOW I ACTUALLY GOT INTO PRISON, THERE IS A LAW AGAINST THAT AS I AM STILL HERE, BUT I CAN TAKE YOU ON THE RIDE OF MY LIFE.

HOLD ON TIGHT!

Thanks for reading ♪
Krysta Cox ♥

Beauty

From Within

By Lisa Autumn a.k.a. William Lewis

139

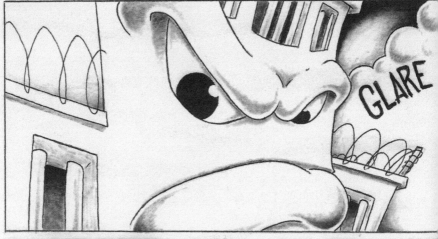

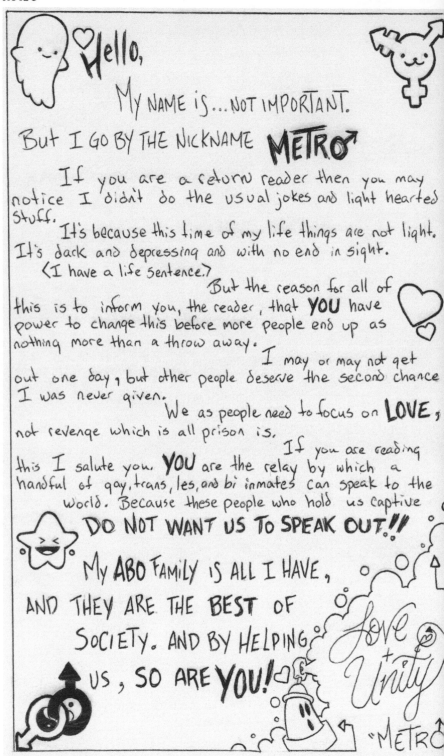

Hello,

My name is... NOT IMPORTANT.

But I go by the nickname **METRO**

If you are a return reader then you may notice I didn't do the usual jokes and light hearted stuff.

It's because this time of my life things are not light. It's dark and depressing and with no end in sight.

⟨I have a life sentence.⟩

But the reason for all of this is to inform you, the reader, that **YOU** have power to change this before more people end up as nothing more than a throw away.

I may or may not get out one day, but other people deserve the second chance I was never given.

We as people need to focus on **LOVE**, not revenge which is all prison is.

If you are reading this I salute you. **YOU** are the relay by which a handful of gay, trans, les, and bi inmates can speak to the world. Because these people who hold us captive

DO NOT WANT US TO SPEAK OUT!!

My **ABO** Family is all I have, and they are the **BEST** of society. And by helping us, so are **YOU!**

Love + Unity

°METRO

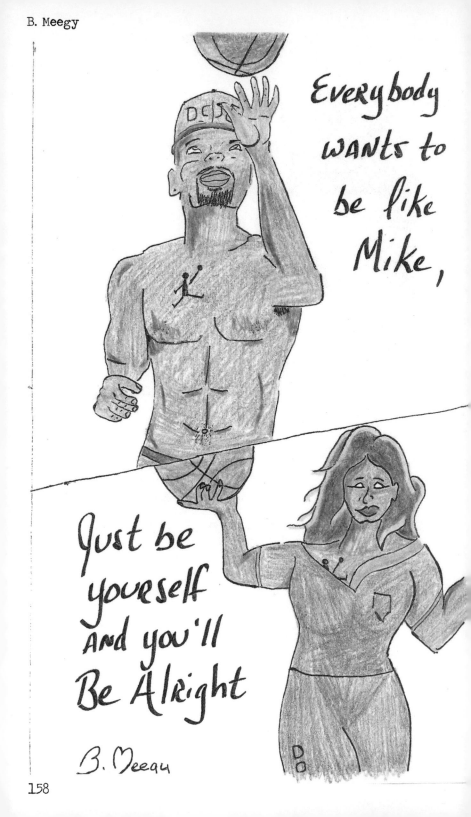

B. Meegy

You
Do Not
Need to
Fight

Every
Perceived
Slight

B. Meegy

Be
a light to shine
I'm A GAY FOR the
STAY. YOU CAN't
Change that...

IN THE HENHOUSE!

By: Jóanlisa Red Cloud-Featherston

A true relationship to start repairing is within yourself.

Sure you have family and what few friendships you've grown close over the years.

The majority of relationships that you do get involved with is usually 95% of the time only interested in canteen or sex25 that you get only. Or are very abusive and want to be the alpha at all times. But they say they love ou ... until they find another victim.

I love you, when do you shop?

I'll see you later, Thanks for making sure I have 90% of your canteen!

Did you know that most of women that come to prison has so much low self esteem of themselves. That already targets them as future victims of abuse from preditors that lurk inside the walls of prison.

175

I thought she had a ton of property before, I wonder why this thug wanted to P.C. up?

Those who start off being the "hunter" in this type of setting. Only end up being the "hunted." Someone will want to challenge you for the thrown. But what kind of queendom is prison life. A cell and others around that smile in your face... yet as soon as you turn your back, they stab you and take over.

All of a sudden, a large number of younger "Thugs" are going to Ad Seg until a series of investigations are over. Phone recordings are being really monitored, and so is incoming mail. Every one is pointing fingers at everyone else. But most of the time they get to comfortable and get sloppy. They dry snitch on themselves. By using their own products themselves.

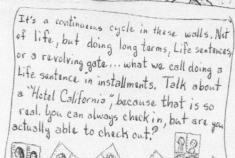

Ha! Ha! Ha! Ha!

It's a continuous cycle in these walls. Not of life, but doing long terms, Life sentences, or a revolving gate... what we call doing a Life sentence in installments. Talk about a "Hotel California", because that is so real. You can always check in, but are you actually able to check out?

Something about this whole system just does not work. Women don't have any support system like men do. When men go to prison, their family stays by their sides and even moves close to where they are. For women, gay men, or transgender are forgotten. Statistics have this motto, "Out of sight, out of mind!" No letters, they won't accept your phone calls. No visits either. Woman just give up.

We all know that the world out there still goes on, and progress. As time goes by, and they see the less of us. They seem to forget we still exist. Then when we write, they wonder why we sound so angry or so extremely sad. Some become so depressed, they end up on heavy duty phsych-meds... looking like a zombie.

Than there are those who just give up all hope, and lose all trust in people. Feeling like the forgotten ones in life. Because people have this mind set that woman... the female should be a nuture/mother/caretaker. That should know better to stay at home. Not in prison! But times have changed, there are nomore "June Cleavers" out there.

Most are second or third generation inmates that grew up within the system. They don't know what a stable family is like. Being raised by their grandparents or foster parents. Some become parents themselves at a very young age. The same person that grew up with any parents around. Usually saw abuse, drug and alcohol use, even sexual abuse on them as a child. To them, that is the normal, because that is all they've known. What is a normal family life supose to be?

Reality! There are over 300,000 new mother under the age of 16 with drugs and sexual abuse.

Some don't even know who the father is, because most likely they were at a party getting high and started dancing and things got out of hand. Or, the girls wanted to make more money so they can get high. So they sell their body for sex. You would be surprised at how old the clients are too! Some are young college kids, but most are old enough to be these girls grandfather.

The babies are born addicted and/or too early. And the mother never bonds with that baby while it's in the hospital. Either she abandons it, or it just dies. Instead of giving that baby a chance. Put it up for adoption so it can be loved by people that can't have children.

But if they do keep the baby, they collect welfare, food stamps, and medical. Get into low income housing, which is usually in the middle where the drugs are available, no rent, no food, and you forget to take the baby to the doctor. The Child Protective Services get involved & so does family court.

Being in the system is a hard road to be on. But you can change the out come of it.

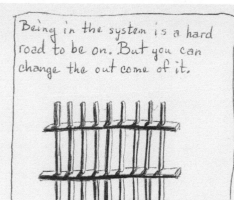

Either hard times, and become a revolving gate by keeping coming back until you do get a life sentance.

Or you can finally wake up and start groups to better yourself. Get an education and learn a trade to get a job once you parole. AA/NA, Parenting skills, Life Skills It is all free in prison, take advange of it while you are here.

Since the odds are set up against us from the day we enter prison. It's a great feelin to prove them wrong, and that you are worth it. Because you did the work and completed it. Now, it's time to set your plans, life once you parole.

The key thing is don't give up on yourself. Just because no-one was there for you when you were young. Don't mean you can't be there for yourself. It's time to look for all the positives... Instead of only finding all the negatives in life.

You just have to remind yourself which will be better for your well being. Putting yourself in the frying pan. Or working at growing in towards freedom. Making a life for yourself.

Seek a mentor that will stir you in the positive direction in your life. Find someone who found out the hard way. They have a story to teach you.

Sure... there are always going to be haters. But like the saying goes... "Haters make you famous!"

Just know that you are the only one that creates your own destany. Where are you going to put all of your hard work at the end? Who will benefit from it?

This is a school of hard knocks, so take advantage of all the free education, and free vocational training that you can get in prison.

Your goal is to get out of this Hen House forever. Get your own nest out there and become your own success.

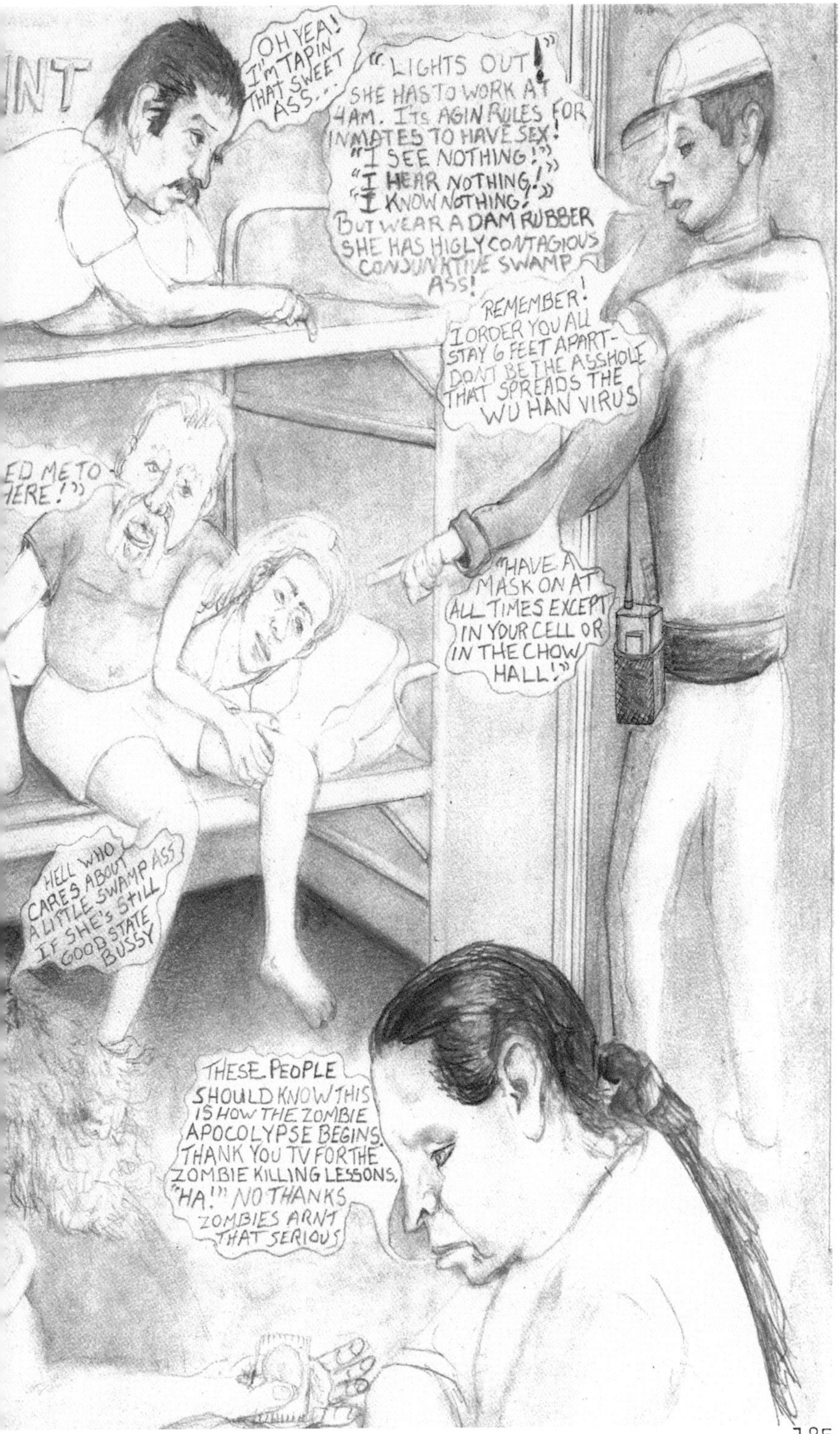
INT
OH YEA! I'm TAPIN THAT SWEET ASS...
"LIGHTS OUT!" SHE HAS TO WORK AT 4AM. Its AGIN RULES FOR INMATES TO HAVE SEX! "I SEE NOTHING!" "I HEAR NOTHING!" "I KNOW NOTHING!" BUT WEAR A DAM RUBBER SHE HAS HIGLY CONTAGIOUS CONJUNKTIVE SWAMP ASS!
REMEMBER! I ORDER YOU ALL STAY 6 FEET APART- DON'T BE THE ASSHOLE THAT SPREADS THE WU HAN VIRUS
ED ME TO HERE!"
"HAVE A MASK ON AT ALL TIMES EXCEPT IN YOUR CELL OR IN THE CHOW HALL!"
HELL WHO CARES ABOUT A LITTLE SWAMP ASS IF SHE'S STILL GOOD STATE BUSSY
THESE PEOPLE SHOULD KNOW THIS IS HOW THE ZOMBIE APOCOLYPSE BEGINS. THANK YOU TV FOR THE ZOMBIE KILLING LESSONS. "HA!" NO THANKS ZOMBIES ARNT THAT SERIOUS

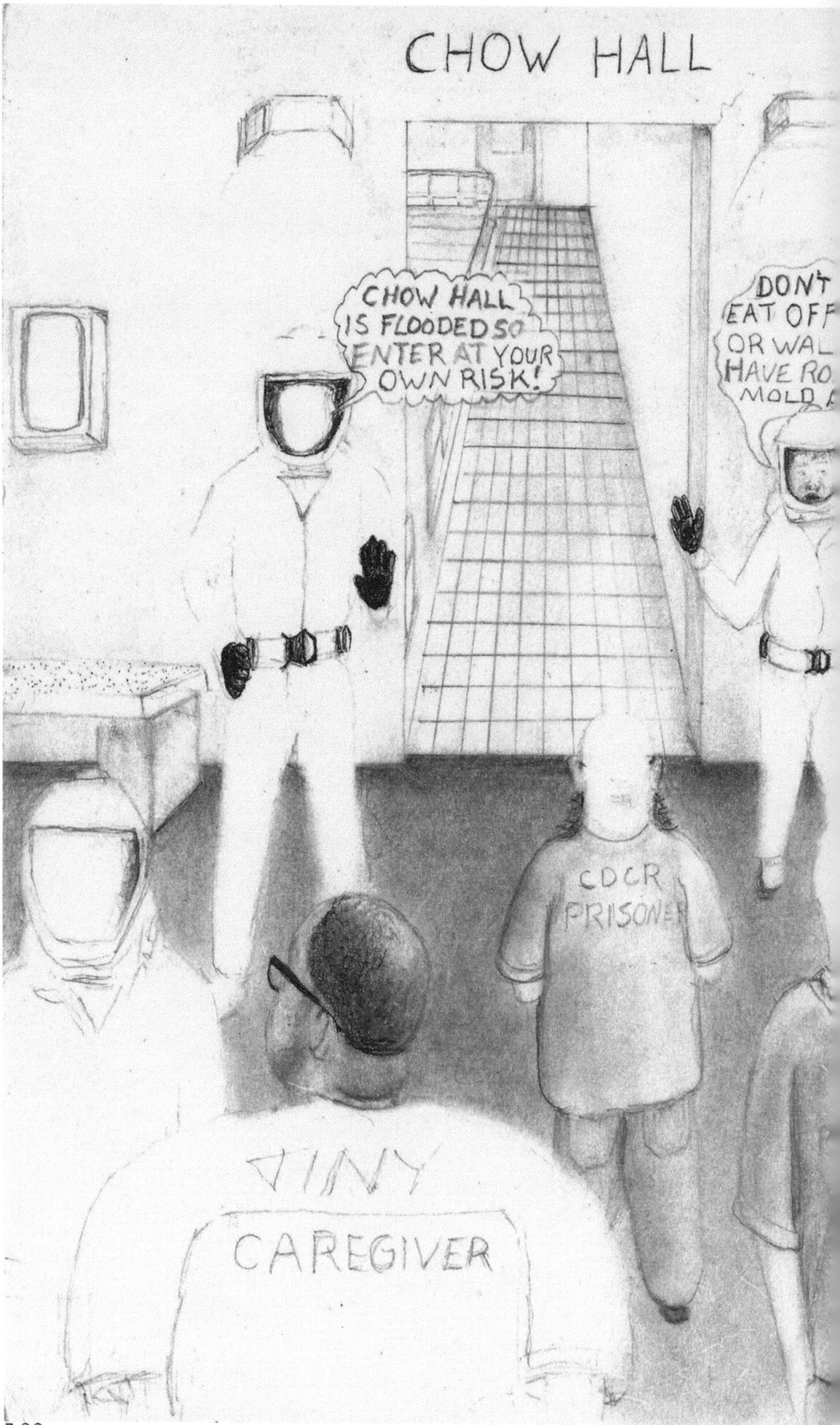
CHOW HALL
CHOW HALL IS FLOODED SO ENTER AT YOUR OWN RISK!
DON'T EAT OFF OR WAL HAVE RO MOLD
CDCR PRISONE
TINY
CAREGIVER

STOP DREAMING BOUT ANYWHERE OUTSIDE OF HELL! GET OUT IN THE DINNING ROOM NOW. I WANNA HEAR ALL THEIR COMPLAINTS ABOUT THE FOOD!
WEAR YOUR MASK

OH NO!, I think my friend Jerell here has THE WU HAN!
"YEP" Ah! I'm HAVING TROUBLE BREATHING!

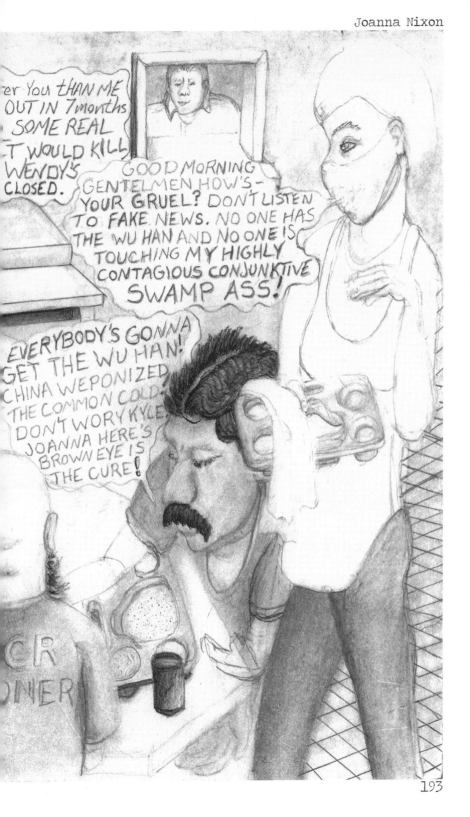

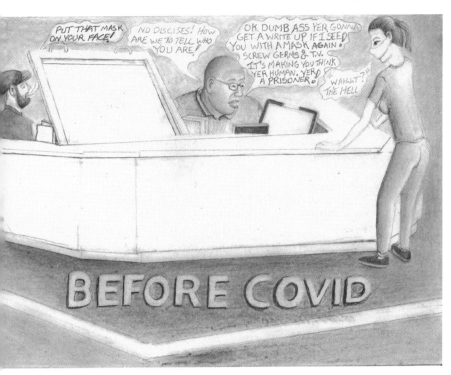

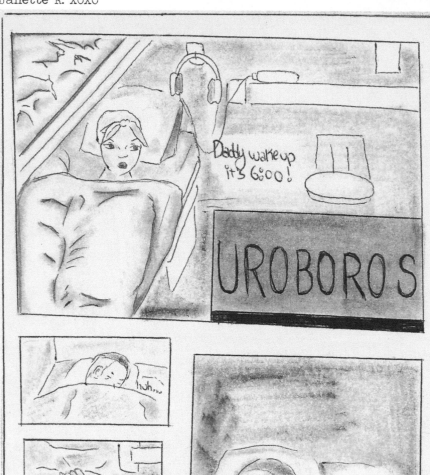

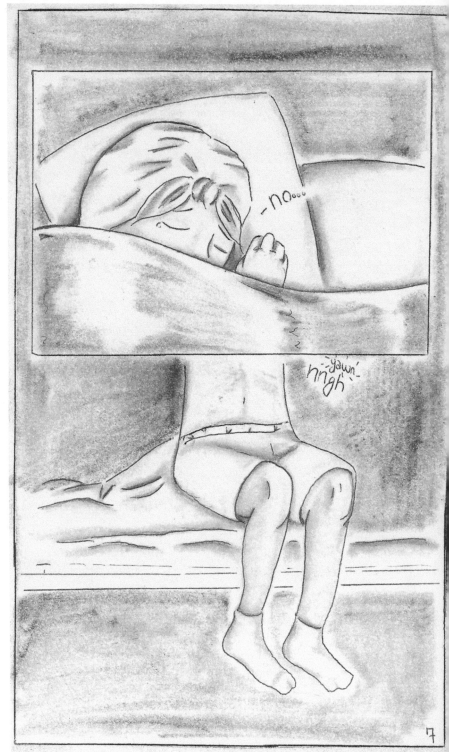

208

Starting
with changing
yourself

is the
first step
in the
process

of making the world
a better place

The walls of people's minds are the greatest obstacles we have to face

These walls
will fall in
rubble;
if not
literally
than
allegorically

Imagine how incredible
this world could be
if people weren't
held back by
their own minds
and negative
self
images

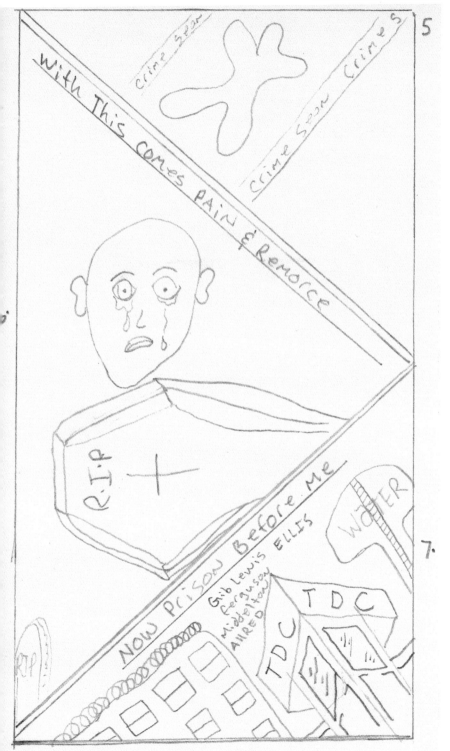

with This COMES pain
7.
I DESERVE TO DIE.
I DONT WANT TO LIVE.
No more wife, No faily will write, What EVER CREated Human Kind Has abandond ME....
-NIN-
NOW I'M Nothing
I focus on the pain, the only Thing thats real
8.
am I To BLAME

COME TO PEACE WITH MY PAST

INCEST, MOLESTAION, RAPE
ADULTRY, DRUGS, MURDER ......

WELL PRETTY
FUC#EN MUCH
EVERY THING
YOU COULD
FATHEM !

NOW THREW NEW THINGS I GROW

·Books·
·People·

·ART·

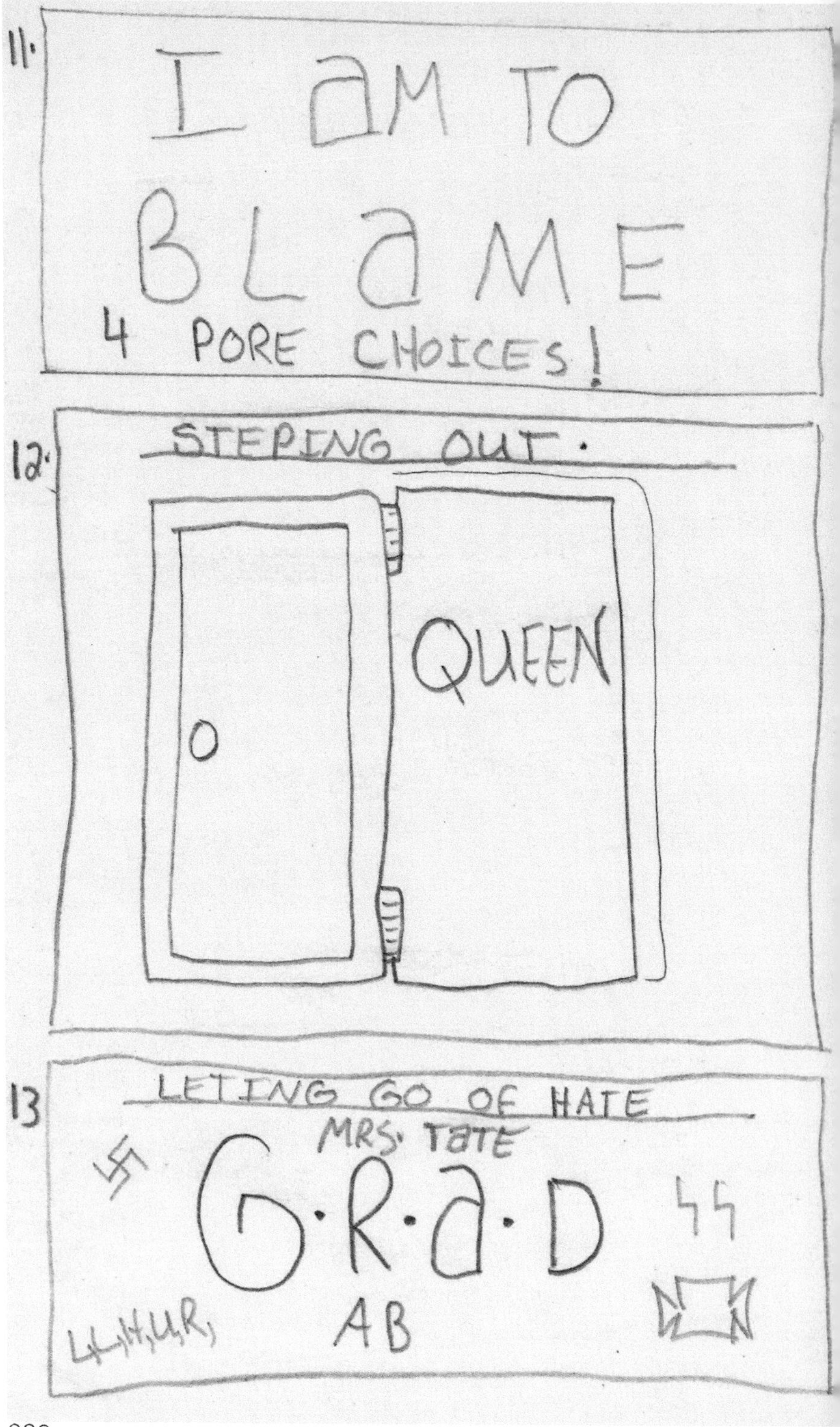

11. **I am to BLAME 4 PORE CHOICES!**

12. STEPING OUT.

QUEEN

O

13. LETING GO OF HATE

MRS. TATE

G·R·a·D

AB

HEY YA'LL

THIS SECOND SUBMISSION WAS A LONG TIME IN COMING. LITERAL TEARS AND OVER A YEAR OF FRUSTRATION WAS ENOUGH TO DRIVE ME FRACKING CRAZY!

ABOUT A YEAR AND TWO MONTHS AGO I GOT INTO A FIGHT. LIKE MOST FIGHTS IT WAS OVER SOMETHING STUPID. LONG STORY SHORT I WAS HIT SQUARE DEAD CENTER IN MY ONE GOOD EYE, WHICH FROM WHAT THE DOCTORS SAY CAUSED A "TRAUMATIC CATARACT."

NOT A GOOD DIAGNOSIS FOR SOMEONE WITH VERY POOR VISION

THE DECLINE IN VISION WAS SWIFT. IT WASN'T LONG UNTIL NORMAL EVERYDAY ACTIVITIES BECAME A STRUGGLE.

THEN WORSE HAPPENED... I WASN'T ABLE TO DRAW! WHAT USE TO TAKE ME MINUTES TO DO STARTED TO TAKE HOURS *GRRRR*

HUE, TEXTURE, DEPTH, CONTRAST, PROPORTION AND LINE QUALITY WERE ALL THROWN OUT THE WINDOW.

FADE TO BLACK DOESN'T QUITE HIT ON IT BUT IT COMES DAMN CLOSE * ♥ * ♡

AND THROUGH IT ALL WAS CASPER *, HE WAS LITERALLY MY LIGHT AT THE END OF THE TUNNEL

FOR MONTHS HE HECKLED, HAR-
ASSED, VEXED AND POSSIBLY THREAT-
ENED MEDICAL UNTIL SURGERY WAS
FINALLY PERFORMED.

WHILE AT THE SAME TIME PROVIDING
ME ~ 👀 WITH NEEDED HOPE AND
INSPIRATION.

NEEDLESS TO SAY THIS "CON *NECTION"
IS DEDICATED TO CASPER FOR HIS
"Love", ENERGY AND COMPASSION. ALL
OF WHICH HE USES TO MAKE **ALL** OF HIS
CONTRIBUTORS FEEL SPECIAL, WANTED
AND NEEDED.

HOPE YOU ENJOY THIS NEXT EDITION.
IN LIGHT, LOVE AND SOLIDARITY ♡.

SCARY MOVIE
3·21·20

SPECIAL SHOUT OUT:
CARLA
KINOKO
METRO
PROMISE
DANNY
AMBER
G-MONEY
SCORPIO

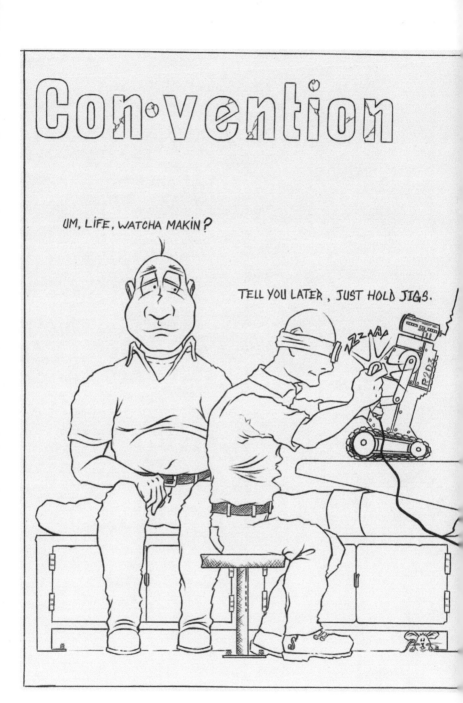

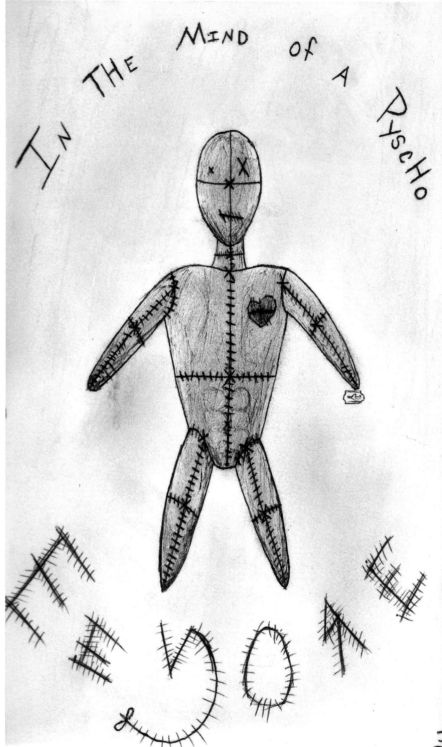

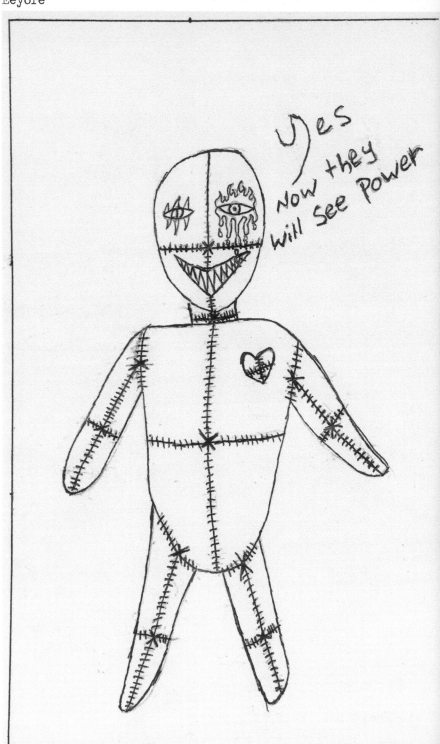

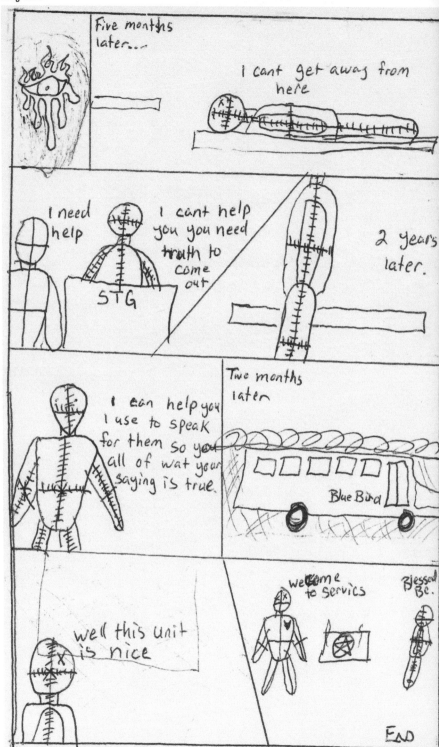

A Homo Thug PrisoneR's

PTSD

by: Sirbrian Spease
"A proud Homo Thug."

"How dare u come to church faggot!"
"Trans-women love the Lord."
"I must be hear-ing things!"
PRISON
D.C
"If I see u walkin with us I'm gonna straight punch u."
"I Know I got a brown crayon some where, to help me hide the bruises. Got to look good for the Lord."
D.OC
D.O.C
1

"Save her! Save her! My child!"
"I can feel her pain! Make it stop."
"If she gets hit one more time with that locking sock, she is dead."
PRISON
"Okay! Fuck I'm going! she ain't gonna die."
"About time u came to your senses
"It's probably to late."
PRISON

"You got a lot of salt in your chet."
"Yo I'm not a piece of chicken! Yo take your meds."
"I am out!!"
HT
PRISON
PRISON
It is over!!!
"Don't Kill me! I won't be gay!!"
"I am a homo thug you are safe!!
D.O.C
5
PRIS

"Please tell me that you don't have a wifey boy."
HT
"I do, sorry."
D.O.C
"Why she got to be the lucky one?
"You are my strength!"
"You are my power!"
HT
6
D.O.C
PRISON
"She's not the lucky one! I am."
HT

EVER SINCE HE WAS A YOUNG PUPPY SPARK WANTED TO BE A FIREDOG...

①

HE LOOKED UP TO THE REAL FIREDOGS AND BECAME FRIENDS WITH MANY OF THEM...

②

③ AS HE GOT OLDER SPARK STUDIED EVERYTHING HE COULD ABOUT BEING A FIREDOG...

④ SPARK FINALLY GOT HIS CHANCE WHEN THE FIRE DEPARTMENT HAD OPENINGS. SPARK TOOK AND PASSED THE REQUIRED TESTS...

BUT BECAUSE HE WAS GAY SPARK WAS NEVER FULLY ACCEPTED AND WAS OFTEN SHUNNED BY THE OTHER FIREDOGS...

⑤

FIRE DEPARTMENT

FEELING LONELY, SPARK DISCOVERED THE WORLD OF INTERNET PORNOGRAPHY, WHICH EVENTUALLY LED TO CUB PORN...

⑥

⑦ SPARK WAS ARRESTED, CONVICTED AND SENTENCED TO 235 MONTHS AT ELKTON POUND...

⑧ FEELING LONELY AS EVER, SPARK WONDERED IF ANYONE STILL LOVED AND CARED FOR THIS FORMER FIREDOG...

ELKTON POUND

SPARK 2020

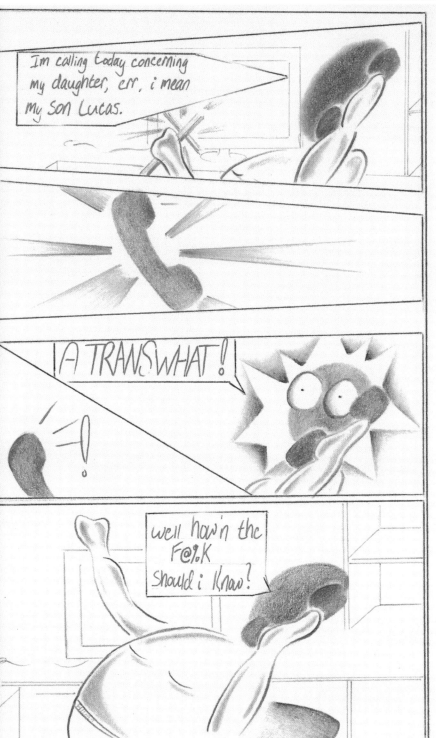

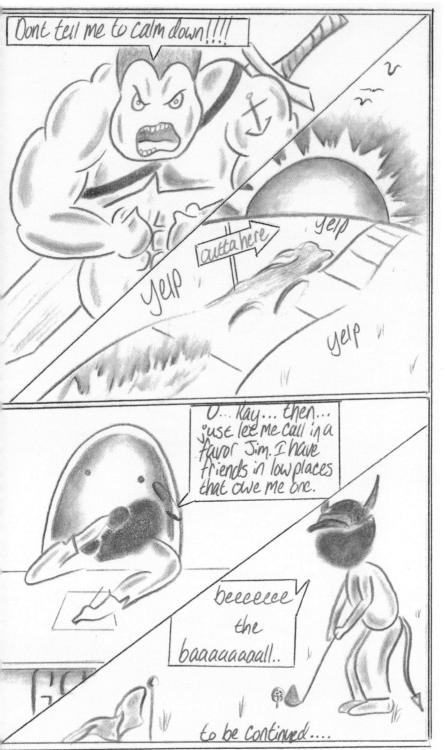

all text by Panagioti Tsolkas
courtesy of the Abolishionist

I want to think about prisons within the framework of industrial extraction

Pangioti Tsolkas is a founder/coordinator of the Campaign to Fight Toxic Prisons, a former editor of the Earth First! Journal, a direct action trainer and a father of two.

Instead of extracting resources from underground, they are extracting people from their neighborhoods and communities...

and creating an
industry that
serves political
and commercial
interests ...

It's unfortunately the norm to treat people in prison as disposable

and to

put them in places that are considered sacrifice zones

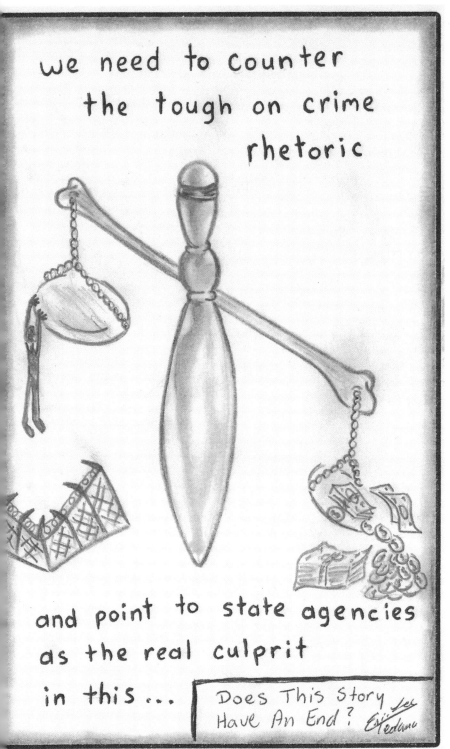

E.L. Tedana

we need to counter the tough on crime rhetoric

and point to state agencies as the real culprit in this ...

Does This Story Have An End?

E.L. Tedana

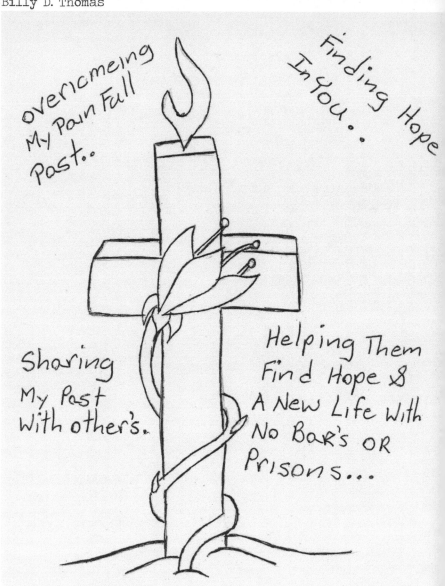

Overicmeing My Pain Full Past..

Finding Hope In You..

Sharing My Past With other's.

Helping Them Find Hope & A New Life With No Bar's OR Prisons...

I am #1275621 Billy D. Thomas I Have Found Faith That Helps me over come all my Past, From Being CPS imprisoned Raped and give capitol life in Texas Prison Then my moms Death and CoViD-19

Robert Welch

298

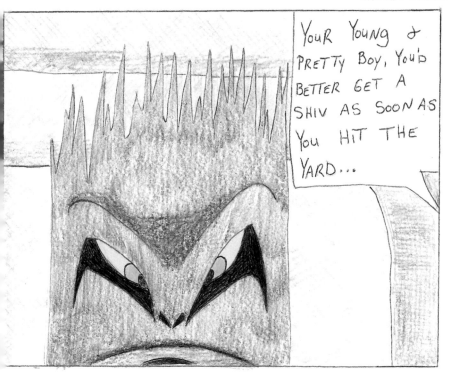

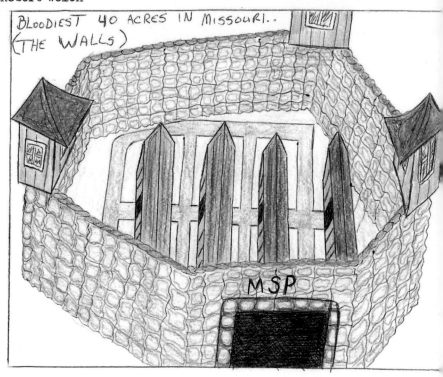

WELCOME TO BIRDCAGE
LINE UP BOTH YOU LADIES!
SHUT YOUR MOUTH!!
HE'S SO RUDE!
DID HE JUST CALL US LADIES?
YA! WHY?
MEN'S SHOWERS
WOW I'M IMPRESSED!
CAUSE I'M BI-SEXUAL!
ME TOO!
1

SO WHAT'S YOUR NAME?
I'M PICKLE "D"
I'M TACO BE-MAN A SUPER HERO!
What's A SUPERHERO LIKE YOU DOING HERE?
I'M UNDERCOVER..
CAN'T EXPLAIN SHOOOO...
I CAN KEEP SECERTS
HERE COMES SOMEONE
WARDEN
WHO'S TACO?
COME TO MY OFFICE NOW!!!
I'M PUTTING YOU IN REGULAR POPULATION!
HELLO TACO
TO BAD I SAY WHAT GO'S!
YOUR SUPPOSE TO PUT ME WITH MY GENDER GROUP!!!
YOU WON'T GET AWAY WITH THIS!
TAKE HIM TO THE DUNGEON!
YOU ARE VIOLATING MY RIGHTS!
SAID NO! TACO FOOL!
NOW GUARDS TAKE HIM AWAY...
YOU DON'T KNOW WHO I AM...
2

THE DUNGEON BIRDCAGE
WHOS THAT???
THAT, YOU TACO!
YES!
HOW DID YOU GET OVER HERE PICKLED!
THEY BEAT ME UP!
WHO DID THIS TO YOU!
TELL ME WHO!
THE...
OK THE GUARDS!
RAHHHH...
WOW!
MY HERO!
YOU ARE A SUPERHERO
I'M HERE FOR YOU!
I OWE U A FAVOR
LIKE A BACKRUB!
YA
I'LL TAKE ONE NOW!
LAY DOWN I GOT U!
NOT TO HARD OK!
I WON'T OK...
HMM TACO YOU LOOK SO GOOD TO EAT!
NOTHING
HEY WHAT IS GOING ON IN HERE!
DAMN!

???
HAHA TACO YOU FOOL!
YOU CAN'T GET AWAY
GRRRR..
TAKE THESE 2 AWAY, CAPTAIN!
MY PLEASURE WARDEN I'M PUTTING THESE 2 LOVE BIRDS IN A SPECIAL PLACE! HAHA
(BUT RIGHT NOW LET'S PLAY ALONG OK!
I HOPE SO!
DONT WORRY I HAVE A PLAN MY PICKLE DARLING
STICK WITH ME!
OK..
CELL 1
CELL 2
HA HA HA
YOU 2 ARE DOIN A WEE
MY TACO I HOPE HE GETS US OUT OF HERE!
BACK TO SQUARE ONE!
5

OK I AGREE

YES

I CAN HEAR YOU MY LOVE! LET'S DO A WEEK IN HERE AND SEE WHERE WE GO!

YOU THERE PICKLE?

I HAD TO TELL YOU THIS IS BREAKING ME WITHOUT YOU... YOUR MY TACO FILLING!

1 WEEK GO'S BY...

PHONES

WOW! IT'S GP! NOW I CAN GIVE YOU THAT BACK RUB!

AWESOME!!!

AHHH

YOU FILL ME UP!

JUST TOSSING YOUR SALAD...

I NEED TO TELL WHAT IS GOING ON IN HERE ITS SERIOUS!

HUH?!?

HOLD ON SAY WHAT?

LOOK OUT TACO!

SAY GOT BAD NEWS PICKLE IS WITH ME NOW!!!

YA PICKLE CAN'T RESIST THIS HOT IN' SPICY LIKE ME!

6

317

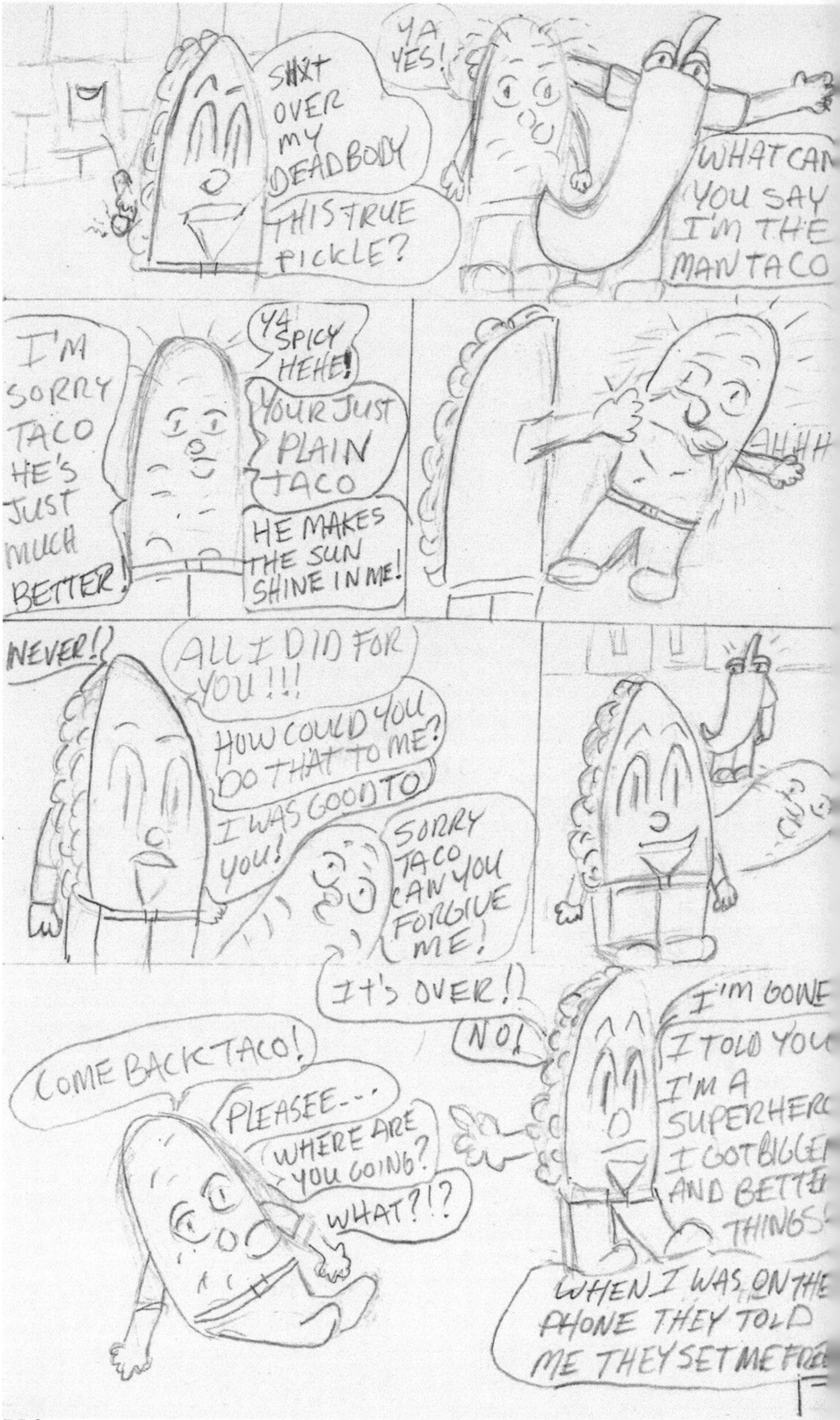
SHXT
OVER
MY
DEADBODY
THIS TRUE
PICKLE?
YA
YES!
WHAT CAN
YOU SAY
I'M THE
MAN TACO
I'M
SORRY
TACO
HE'S
JUST
MUCH
BETTER!
YA
SPICY
HEHE!
YOUR JUST
PLAIN
TACO
HE MAKES
THE SUN
SHINE IN ME!
AHHH
NEVER!
ALL I DID FOR
YOU!!!
HOW COULD YOU
DO THAT TO ME?
I WAS GOOD TO
YOU!
SORRY
TACO
CAN YOU
FORGIVE
ME!
IT'S OVER!
COME BACK TACO!
PLEASEE...
WHERE ARE
YOU GOING?
WHAT?!?
NO!
I'M GONE
I TOLD YOU
I'M A
SUPERHERO
I GOT BIGGER
AND BETTER
THINGS
WHEN I WAS ON THE
PHONE THEY TOLD
ME THEY SET ME FREE

WE ARE AGENTS AND HERE TO SERVE YOU AND PICK UP TACO HE WORKS FOR US!
SAY WHAT!!!
GLAD THATS OVER NOW!
WE GOT TO SEE...
WHAT'S NEXT TACO?
THERE'S BETTER THING'S TO DO. AND I'M HERE TO SAVE THOSE THAT NEED IT! CAUSE I'M SUPER TACO BI-MAN!!!
TO BE CONTINUED...
8

LET'S MAKE FREEDOM RING

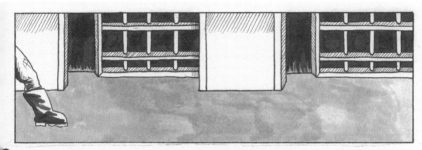

Sometimes I wish that I was never born. Today as I worked in the field I was consumed with **HEAVY** thoughts. Starting to despair and I wonder why this is happening. I **NEVER** dreamed I'd be in this predicament. In this kind of place around these kind of people.

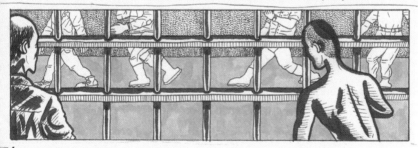

I've discovered how much fear I have within me and it scares me just how unprepared I am to deal with it. I'm very scared and I ain't afraid admitting it. Who do you turn to when everybody is a stranger? I'm learning just how unforgiving a hellhole prison is. Maybe suicide is my only option.....

Angold is ruled by force and violence, with stabbings, rapes and killings the norm. Inmates find themselves trapped, having to stand up and fight or submit. In prison your manhood is challenged 24/7. You had to prove it or lose it. You either get a man or a shank.

Security report to work, offer little or no help, and certainly don't care about who did what to whom. Inmates rule the prison, security is here to prevent escapes.

Imprisonment is degrading enough, but it can be sheer HELL with sexual predators trying to stab you with a HARD cock or a SHARP shank. I may be 100% queer, but that dosen't mean I wanna be a prison whore. I felt weak and helpless in this jungle....

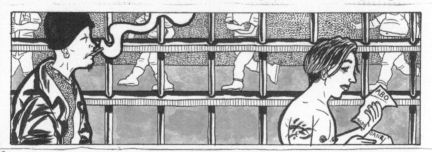

I remember coming in from the field and marveling at the beauty of the sky and the swaying trees. Life never looked so good to me as I walked down the tier to my cell......

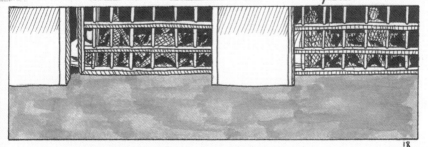

18

Inside of me, fear and indecision tied my insides into a knot. Despite all the weight of the world on my shoulders I managed to walk up the stairs and reach my tier on Upper Right of A-Block. I looked through my cell bars and was startled at the sight of a completely barren cell. All my fear and rage melted away to nothing but confusion......

19

As the celldoor loudly closed I was engulfed with many a question. Where was my cellmate "Impact" and all his property??? Did he move cells or did he get locked up??? Would the convicts think I went to security to get rid of him??? Should I expect violent attacks against me???

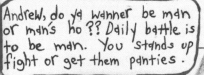

Andrew, do ya wanner be man or man's ho?? Daily battle is to be man. You stands up fight or get them panties.

Friends is nothing but trouble. Ain't no love or friends. They both be enemies to d man.

If any man proach yd foul dat vierldte yer manhood ye must be reddy to make's exdmple. In short order Andrew. Don't ya have pity or mercy for none will see ye. All yd get in joint is hard dick or sharp shank. Let me tell you story of Joseph, he got here same day....

1982

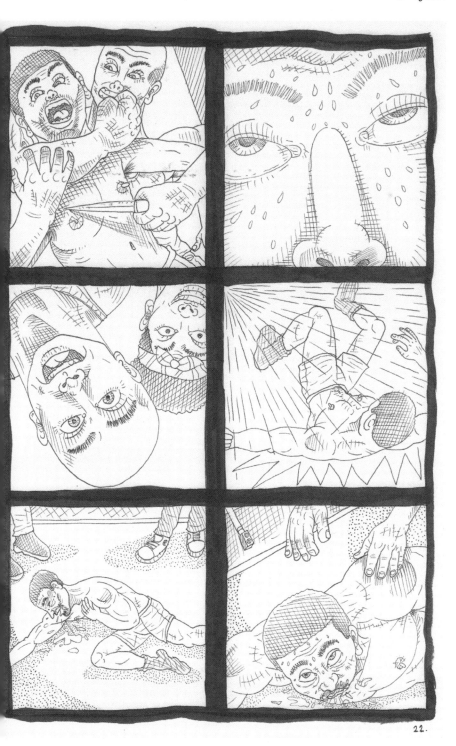

22.

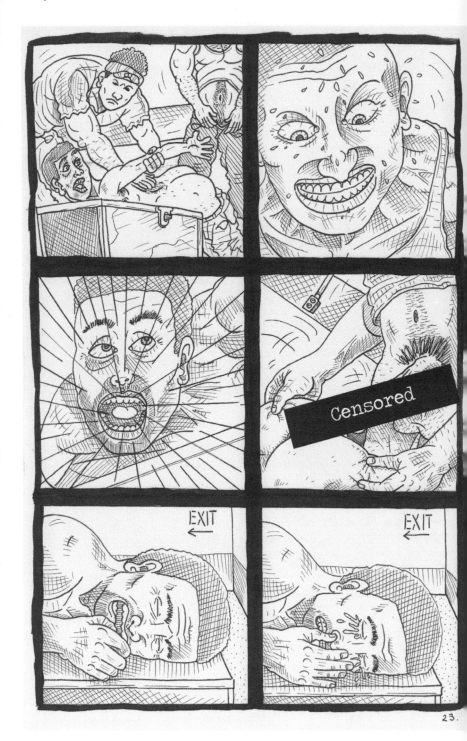

23.

All desé years I blame me! Joseph and me rodd bus to Angold. Dat wuz de first night in dorm. He slept bed over. When he got grabbed up I was glad it wasn't me.......

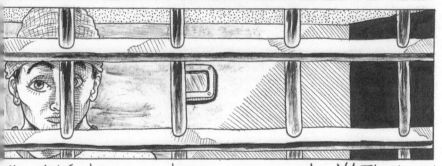

He didń have no chance wit no shank! They used no grease on him and dey used him like a girl all night. He bled so bad dey had to sew him up. His olé man wuz HARD on her. She was pimped out to any man for a pack of smokes.

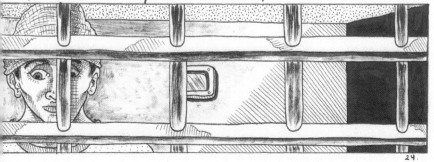

24.

Hector's voice was in my ears, long after he walked away. That story of Joseph had me so sick to my stomach that I vomited. Nobody deserves to get beat up and raped. Tragically, Joseph later was shanked to death by her "ole man" for "disobedience." What a crying shame............

I can understand how Hector blames himself, but it would of been his fate if he tried to intervene. After that night Hector slept with phonebooks taped to him. He got him a shank the next day and had to use it many a time when the rape gang pulled up on him. His advice to me was to either get a strong man or a shank. He couldn't help me.......

25.

found out what happened to Impact. One of the "rats" turned him in because he refused to pay his debt on some dope. The note said he had drugs, but after tearing the cell apart none were found. A shank did turn up and in his box. Otherwise, we would of both been wrote up and locked up. He got found guilty and moved to Camp J, the punishment camp for the whole prison. Worst of the worst.

Hector gave me much to think about. I appreciate him trying to help me. I also understand that he blames himself for Joseph getting "turned out" and that drove him to try and help me. I didn't see any sense in divulging that I was gay to him. He's "old school" and wouldn't understand or accept. As a queer I don't have many choices. I can get a shank or get a strong man. Or, I could hide in the "closet" and pretend to be a "real" man. I looked through my cell bars and out the window, feeling a sad unease wondering how exactly I ended up here..........

26.

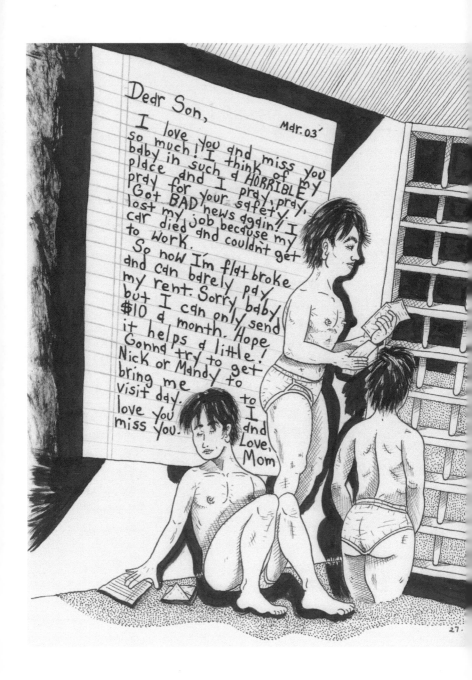

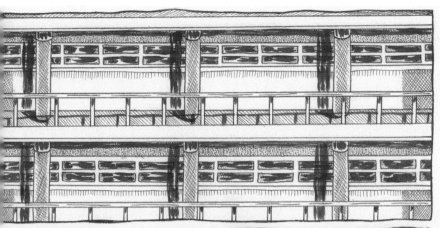

Reading Mom's letter makes me think of Home. Such thoughts only make me ache with LONELINESS. Being free at home seems like a lifetime ago. Like a long dream deteriorating into a NIGHTMARE.

Maybe, if I go to sleep, I will wake up back at home, where I belong.
I do find relief turning my mind to the past. I lie awake thinking about my family and "friends." I tend to bury myself in memories, especially of my youth......

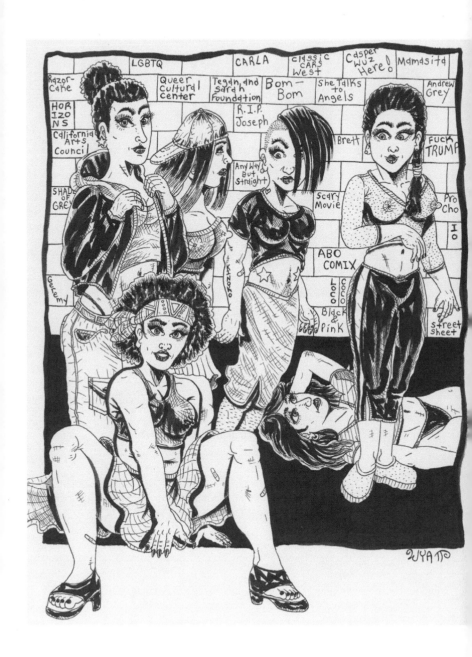

Lisa Autumn

Hiya! It's Daxter again and welcome to the Second Installment to "The Fallen Eagle." In this Second Part, we'll delve into my time of struggles in Prison, the good times and the bad.

THE FALLEN EAGLE

PART 2
BY:
DAXTER
SNOWPAW

Daxter Snowpaw

But there was a lot of trust issues between us. I had gotten into trouble by him so many times. We had broken up later that year. It was really hard.

So I wandered around aimlessly for 3 years. It felt like that nobody wanted me. I felt like I was nobody.

SAVED BY WOLF AND CAT

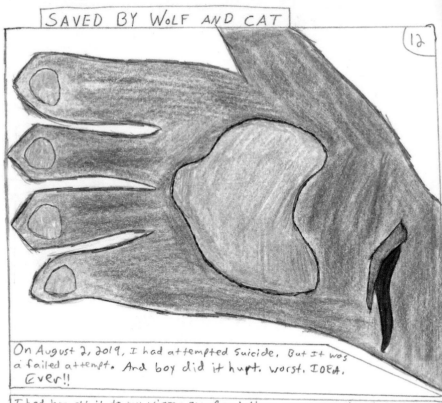

12

On August 2, 2019, I had attempted suicide. But It was a failed attempt. And boy did it hurt. worst. IDEA. Ever!!

I had brought it to my wiccan group and there was a great relief when a wolf named Kowa and a Panther there named Kitar had saved me. They had Picked me up and "adopted me."

13

And it was on August 2nd, that I rededicated myself to the craft and Practice and on that day I dedicated myself to being a loyal pup and better friend as Kowa and Kitar took me under their wing to help me Out. And its them along with Kiba that I wanted to thank for being there for me and helping me Pull through the good times and the bad. And now I'm on my way home to restart my life. Thank you guys for being there for me. I miss you and love you furever and fur always. And thank you to all the furs for your support and to ABO for helping me get my experiences out there. ~ Dax

END

15

DEDICATION PAGE

THIS PAGE, I WANT TO DEDICATE TO MY BAND THAT I STARTED WHILE LOCKED UP CALLED "THE PAC."

ON PAGE 05, PANEL'S 9, 10, and 11, I referenced a song that we all created and I wanted to give credit where credit is Due:

SONG: "I'll MAKE YOU FAMOUS".
WRITERS: DANNY E., LARRY B., and David H.
MUSIC: DAVID H., LARRY B., Alan J. and Judas.
HARMONY: Daxter S. (ME: Robert E.)

"THIS SONG was made and should be credited to all in the band that no matter what happened, in the end, we all put our energy into the song and it belongs to all of us.
Thank you guys for giving me the chance to play a part in this."

"This song had different meanings for everybody.
For me, the trauma I went through with the 3 yrs with Soarin."

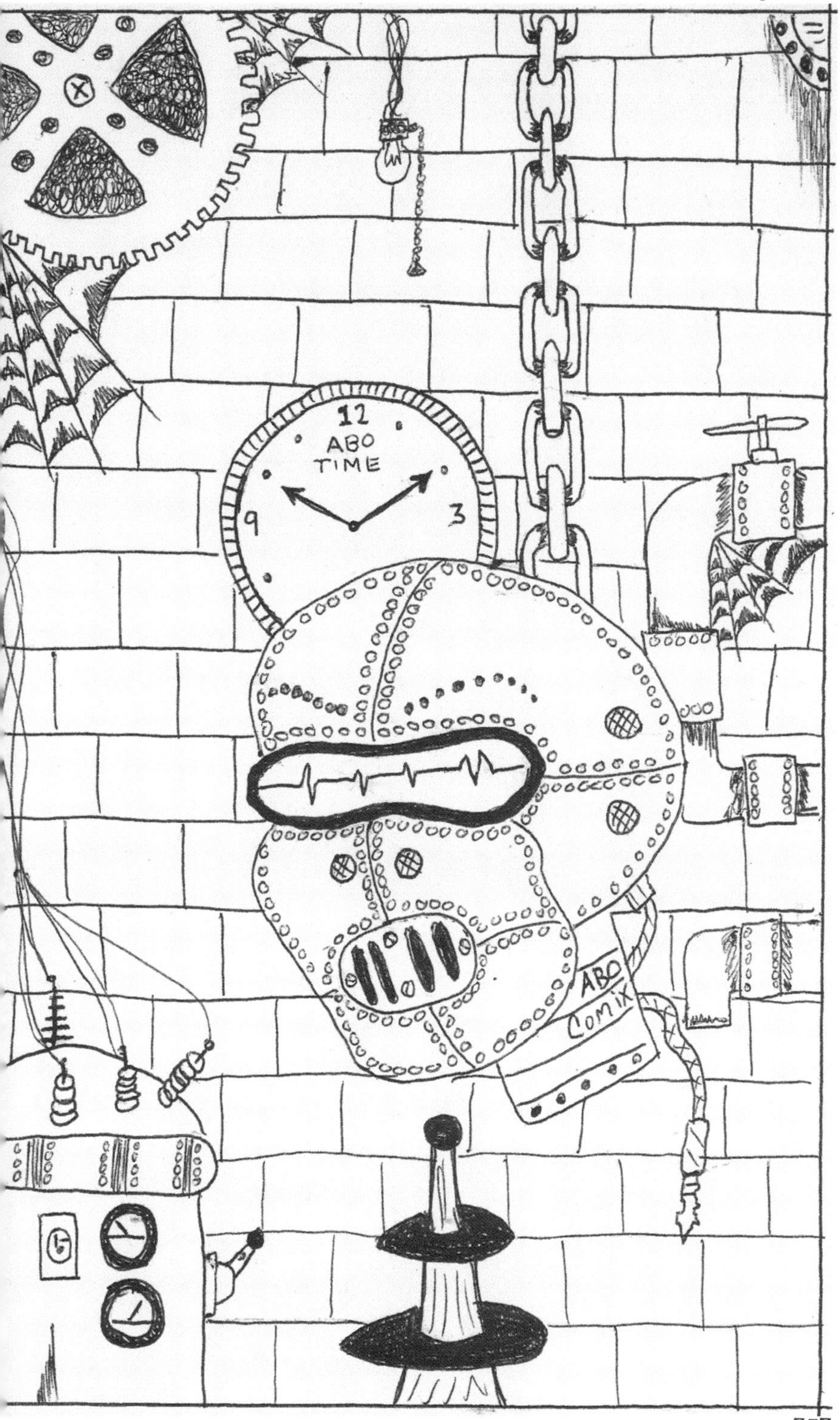
12
ABO
TIME
9
3
ABO
COMiX

RAWRRR!

A Monster is Rampaging thru Tokyo, making it the 3rd time this week. A local had this to say...

It could be **WORSE**, we could have **TRUMP** as a leader

CLiCK

AND NOW WE RETURN TO THE **MOVIE** OF THE **WEEK**

HORNY POTTER AND THE SORCERER'S BONE

WOW POTTER!

THAT WAND IS **HUGE!!** CAN I TOUCH IT?

BOING!

ABO Comix PRESENTS: Hot GUY on a Table!

FOR MORE VISIT WWW.abocomix.com

SEND LOTS OF LOVE and SUPPORT!

Then the bitch says "You're A FRUIT," can you beleave that!?

PeeP!

You've been an amazing friend and great supporter in this short time we've known one another. And for that, from the bottom of my heart I mean it when I say I love you and thank you. I look forward to a future with you as a friend, someone special in my life. You inspire me to become a better person.

I Love You and The Family At ABO You all Have Been a Blessing To US GTBLQ Here in Texas state prison. I Can only Hope The Art I Have Sent With The are That I am sending You This 2020 Will move some ones Hart in Funding My Case on appill and or mentoring me as I over cum and Heal, From The Damige of The mental Health meds and The Sexual abuss While in The Cear of Texas CPS office

I have found that often times when I try to help others, I myself seem to prosper. There is a paradox of positive energy which seems to help everything bloom. An example of this is like: when I try to find an answer to a question for somebody; then I inadvertantly stumble upon some interesting information for myself. We all learn and grow! ☺

I got the vol 3 and let me tell you, it feel so good to know I've acomplished something. Being in prison and to achieve something as being published, something I've always dreamed of and ABo and Staff made it all posiable for me, thank all of ya'll. I'm already planing The Fional part of The Mask and more. I'm also sketching out a drawing as a gift for ABo and all who has made my dreams come true.

I just miss y'all's J-pays, and the pictures you're all so kind enough to send me. You guys make me feel like there's someone out there who cares about me, You guys were my very first REAL correspondence. My first pen-pals.

Thanks for all the encouragement b/c it really helps fuel all my work. Everybody needs inspiration & encouragement & that's doubly true for me. A big part of me is that young boy drawing his heart out hoping to prove that I have talent & value. (Maybe that's why I work so hard) My low-self-esteem always told me that I would never amount to nothing. If I wasn't incarcerated I like to think I'd be at Oisney or OC comics doing what I always dreamed of.

And in addition, I would like to thank ABO Comix for affording me the opportunity to receive ABO Comix Volume 2 edition. Absolutely loved it. It was not only comical but very informative, creatively compelling, and beautifully constructed. Definitely a 5 star! And something to be shared across this polarized nation. I can't wait to see more.

Thank you so much for putting me in this years Anthology. My mom was thrilled to have heard I finally got published. Hopefully this little bit will spark a career or side career for being a Published Author.

You are appreciated, so much so! I am most grateful & thankful to have been blessed with you & all there in life as I have been! You're all wonderful! Thanks, straight from the heart!

Congratulations again on everything & the office/gallary looks great. Just think of where ABO started just 3½ short years ago Wow! I think you've all leveled up ‼ and gained some special powers along the way. I look forward to year 4 and beyond &

JUST A SMALL WAY TO SAY THANK YOU. IT'S THE SMALL THINGS THAT MATTER IN LIFE

I do selfishly wish we could correspond more but I do know you are out there doing amazing work in the world. I mean you can't be friends with Superman then be mad when he leaves his clothes in your living room and the neighbors complain about some dude in tights and a cape flying in and out of your window. Hey it comes with the territory so you just keep being Superman and I'll pick up your clothes and cover for you on the flying out the window thing. But all joking aside I am truly greatful to call you my friend, Thank you so much

I Pray, this letter finds You & Those You Care about happy, healthy & Richly blessed. I Consider myself blessed to have You as a friend!

I HAVE FAITH IN YOU, BELIEVE IN WHAT YOU DO AND ADMIRE YOU FOR WHAT YOU'VE ALREADY DONE. IN THAT VEIN I WILL (SOON, MY FRIEND, SOON) CONTINUE TO SEND YOU NEW CARTOONS AND WILL REDRAW ANY THAT YOU REQUEST.

FOR THE MOST PART I AM ALIVE AND BREATHING. DOING MY BEST TO KEEP MY HEAD UP AND STAY CENTERED. REALLY IF IT WASN'T FOR THE LOVE AND SUPPORT FROM YOU ALL AT ABO COMIX, I WOULD HAVE GIVEN UP LONG AGO. SO I THANK YOU FOR THAT.

— give this to
ABO COMIX!

Omy thank you sooo much! So the Zelda Breath of the Wild book came and I was like omy omy oh my gosh!!! The c..o. let me keep the cover on and everything... I had the cheesiest-cheesy smile all day Pony! So thank you soo-soo-much for everything~♡ I truly love you and the rest of the ABO family like this much ♥♥♥♥♥♥♥♥♥♥♥♥♥♥♥♥♥♥♥♥♥♥♥♥♥♥♥♥

Much Love For ABO Comix ~ it takes alot to do what you all do, and you must have a big heart to accomplish particular things with no ulterior motive, so I made the heart big.

Thank you very much for having such a huge heart. You are a blessing in so many ways. You are a peach!

its realy realy nice To Finnaly read and Feel iF only For a short bit that I am not "weird" That I am part of a loving Family. So please keep up the good work.

PS: Thank you for telling me I did a great job on the portrait, you should of seen, my newest portrait I sent to my mom & dad. I had others here before this lockdown happen all stood around me; even the hardcore artist smiled. It made me feel alive again.

"I felt inspired; my inner Cartoonist has been asleep for some years... you might have woken her up! ☺

COMIX

Thank you for taking interest in my art which if I never got the chance like now, I would be thinking always that I'm a nobody, but with your guidance helping me realize I am a somebody, now I'm going to start my new life in learning and being the best I was made to be.

ABO Comix,

Thank you so much for contacting me - and, treating me like a human... - not, a disposable disproportionate marginalized criminal!

Seriously Casper, from the bottom of my heart I am so Happy for you, the ABO family, & the Cause. I'm very proud to be a member - you have helped me feel like I am normal, good, loved, and a part of something great! Thank you.

Once more, my love and gratitude for the solidarity and support you two are and have been showing to me. I cannot express properly in words what it means to me, but the fact is, this whole experience with ya'll has been life altering and life saving. Should any of you ever need me for anything, know that you will have my loyalty and support.

You all are the best thing yet to ever come into my cell! I hope you all are able to triple double your efforts so that you may be able to reach more people, keep pushing on.

I love all your work and support you do in the LGBTQ community, and I thank you for all you do.

abo
comix
steady
reaching out to the
lgbt community.

You "matter to me" in here. You give us hope. I look forward to a long relationship in friendship with everyone at ABO.

Thanks to the good people at Critical Resistance, last year, I was able to get volume 1 of your book. I thought it was great and very humores. I loved how everyone got a chance to shine: High quality drawings along with ameture art. I'd never seen or read anything like it.

To my surprise I received your letter, submission packet, & the ABO Comix volume 2 & 3. I literally jumped for joy when I saw your books in my stack. So THANK YOU for making my day, week, month, and year. As you might know, we've been on lock down and your books couldn't have come at a better time.

But what I loved the most was the dedication page. I can't even express how much that means to me. Thank you. Thank you for all the love and support. Especially the emotional support. It's uplifting and heart warming. Something greatly needed during the holidays. A million thank yous upon a million thank yous.

I hope y'all like my draws, I'm trying to show my visions more and hope that other's will want to hire me to do work for them. I want to really thank y'all for looking out for me... It's a blessing to have y'all in my corner, I can only hope that my drawings will help to change the minds of those out there who see the worst in life. I only want to change a bad thought to a positive reality... I want y'all to know that I love y'all and see my now and future.

Hey sweetness! Once again, thanks for the sugar comma.' I don't know if you will ever be able to understand how much gratitude is contained in my heart for you and all you have done - and continue to do - for me! Just know that if the world were to end tomorrow that you may regain the cosmos knowing you have left your mark on this world. You are courageous, inventive, and caring. Know that you are greatly loved and appreciated. Never forget: to me you are the greatest friend I've ever had. It is a privilege to have you by my side.

Casper... I have to thank You on broadening my network as I work for and with you... More doors of oppurtunities are opening for me all thanks to God first and secondly for you and others who he has put in my life — You realley make me feel important... especialley during these times... Be strong

I Really, Really, Am grateful to you and yours Foundation for giving a Platform to us Brothers and Sisters who are in this Struggle To Identify, To Survive, To OverCome.

I Love you / ya'll.
(you all) ya'll are the Bomb. Assist Group. & I'm proud to be apart of ya'll.

369

I LOVE YALL VERY, VERY MUCH FOR GIVING ME THIS OPPORTUNITY TO BE ABLE TO DRAW ARTWORK FOR OUR L.G.B.T.Q COMMUNITY ☺!!!!

Make no mistake, this is the most fun I've had in a looooooong time drawing. Really get a chance to put some crazy thoughts to paper! (") lol!!

I will like to say I hope God gives ABO strength to continue on sharing us incarcerated gays through out U.S.A. I hope you really believe when I say that you are the only family must of us have I pray extra hard for God to guide you healthy and safe through this COVID-19 pandemic.

Thank you for all your hard-work and dedication — for giving us this amplification, to express ourselves and share our experiences with the world. It truly makes a difference to have the feeling that we belong some where...

WELL, I REALLY HOPE THAT OUR WORK WILL CONTINUE TO GAIN MOMENTUM AS THE YEAR CLOSES OUT. YOU GUYS HAVE BEEN LIKE GEMS, AND YOU SHINE A RESILIENT MULTI-FACETED LIGHT INTO THE WORLD. THANK YOU FOR BEING YOU, ALL OF YOU.

I LOOK FORWARD TO A FUTURE BEYOND RAZOR-WIRE, AND I SEE YOU AND ALL OUR FAMILY THERE. IT GIVES ME A SENSE OF HOPE AND PURPOSE TO FIGHT DESPERATION. SO KEEP THE WHEELS TURNING.

I really Thank you for in this time of help especially durrin Covid-19 ... Thank you from the bottom of my heart.

How to Help

Thank you for reading these stories. We hope they have inspired you, as they have inspired us, to continue to work towards a better world for all our community members.

If you believe in our mission, you can help support us by:

Donating or providing resources

    paypal.me/abocomix   venmo: @abocomix

    patreon.com/abocomix   cash app: $abocomix

Spreading the word and following us for updates at:

    www.abocomix.com or on Instagram, Facebook & Twitter

Volunteering with us or helping us throw a fundraising event

Writing to someone on the inside:

    If you wish to write to any of our contributors, please go to www.abocomix.com/penpals. Our queer family behind bars would love your feedback, support or friendship.

Talking to friends, family, neighbors & community members:

    Open up a dialogue and remember to meet people where they're at. Don't be afraid of difficult conversations and do your best to maintain an open mind, compassion and understanding. You may learn something new as well. When we know better, we can do better.

Supporting organizations doing the work:

    See the following pages for a list of just some of the many people doing incredible work for people in prison.

Start up your own creative project:

    Against all odds, we're still here. Still creating, still building friendships, and still optimistic about what we can acheive when we work together. Take a chance, work hard and you ill do amazing things.

Resources

Abolition Apostles
A national jail and prison ministry that offers moral and spiritual support to members of the incarcerated community. Assists with pen-pal matches, material support, advocacy, and re-entry.
501 N Jefferson Davis Pkwy, PO Box 791410, New Orleans, LA 791410

Black and Pink
An advocacy organization that matches LGBTQ prisoners with free-world pen-pals and distributes a monthly free newsletter.
2406 Fowler Ave Suite 316, Omaha, NE 68111

Critical Resistance
CR seeks to build an international movement to end the Prison Industrial Complex by challenging the belief that caging and controlling people makes everyone safe. CR also publishes "The Abolitionist," once a year, printed in both English and Spanish, which is free to prisoners.
1904 Franklin Street, Suite 504, Oakland, CA 94612

Trans Pride Initiative
Trans Pride Initiative advocates for trans and gender variant persons in the Dallas area and for incarcerated trans and gender diverse persons throughout Texas. They provide general trans-related information and can answer questions about accessing hormones while doing time. They can also help advocate for improved conditions and safety in prison.
P.O. Box 3982, Dallas, TX 75208

Transgender, Gender Variant, and Intersex (TGI) Justice Project
The TGI Justice Project works primarily with transgender prisoners and formerly incarcerated transgender people in California, and sends out their "Stiletto Prison Newsletter" and their very informative 72-page "Still We Rise-Prison Resource Guide" to all TGI prisoners. TGI also supports TGI prisoners being released to the San Francisco Bay Area, and are part of a broader movement fighting for racial and social justice. They answer letters regularly, but expect delay.
370 Turk St #370, San Francisco, CA 94102

Justice Now
Justice Now focuses on the needs of women prisoners. They work on alternative sentencing, document human rights abuses in prison, provide legal services around women's healthcare access, and offer assistance with compassionate release.
1322 Webster St, #208, Oakland, CA 94612

Human Rights Pen Pals

Human Rights Pen Pals is a grassroots, racial justice community organization, in solidarity with people in California's solitary confinement cells. Through letter writing and community organizing, we promote principled, mutually educational relationships between people in solitary confinement and human rights supporters outside the prison walls.

1301 Clay Street, PO Box 71378, Oakland, CA 94612

Justice Arts Coalition

The Justice Arts Coalition (JAC) is a national network providing information and resources for people creating art in and around the US carceral system.

P.O. Box 8261, Silver Spring, MD 20907

The pARTner Project

The pARTner project is a collaborative effort between The Justice Arts Coalition and Prisoner Express that provides artists on the outside an opportunity to foster connection with artists in prison through letter correspondence and the exchange of creative works.

Justice Arts Coalition, PO Box 8261, Silver Spring, MD 20907

Prison Activist Resource Center

PARC is a prison abolitionist group based on Oakland, California committed to exposing and challenging the institutionalized racism, sexism, ableism, heterosexism, and classism of the Prison Industrial Complex. They correspond with and mail a directory of numerous resources to prisoners, their friends and family members.

PO Box 70447, Oakland, CA 94612

Prisoner Correspondence Project

The Prisoner Correspondence Project is a solidarity project for LGBTQ prisoners in Canada and the U.S., linking them with people part of these same communities outside of prison. Sends information for survival, from harm reduction info to resource guides, from prisoner writing to affirming smut. (note: postage cost increases to Canada from U.S.)

Prisoner Correspondence Project, QPIRG Concordia c/o Concordia University, 1455 de Maisonneuve Ouest, Montreal QC H3G 1M8, Canada

Inside Books Project

Sends free books and literature to prisoners in Texas only. Also sends a very informative prisoner resource guide free to prisoners in all states. Send two stamps, or pre-addressed stamped envelope containing two stamps for a copy of their resource guide.

827 West 12th Street, c/o 12th Street Books, Austin, TX 78701

Tranzmission Prison Project

Tranzmission Prison Project is a queer- and trans-powered prison abolition organization that provides free literature and resources for incarcerated members of the LGBTQ community. Also publishes a queer-friendly
National Prison Resource List.
PO Box 1874, Tranzmission (please list Prison Project in memo)
Asheville, NC 28802

Austin Anarchist Black Cross

Austin ABC works with political and politicized prisoners (LGBTQ+ prisoners, POC prisoners, and prisoners that work to organize through IWOC).
Monkeywrench Books/ABC, 110 E. North Loop Blvd, Austin, TX 78751

Prisoners Literature Project

The Prisoners Literature Project is an all-volunteer, non-profit group that sends free books directly to prisoners who request them from throughout the United States.
c/o Bound Together Books, 1369 Haight St, San Francisco, 94117

LGBT Books to Prisoners

Volunteer-run organization that sends books and other educational materials, free of charge, to LGBT-identified people in prison across the US (except those in TX). Will send books in Spanish (enviar libros en Español).
1202 Williamson St #1, c/o Social Justice Center Incubator
Madison, WI 53703

East Bay Prisoner Support

Sends free anarchist and other literature to prisoners in CA, AZ, NM, TX, UT and NV. Sends zines to queer, trans and women prisoners in any state. Write to receive a catalog.
PO Box 22449, Oakland, CA 94609

Pen Prison Writing Program

The PEN Prison Writing Program believes in the restorative, rehabilitative power of writing and provides hundreds of prisoners across the country with skilled writing teachers and audiences for their work. It provides a place for prisoners to express themselves freely and encourages the use of the written word as a legitimate form of power. PEN's Prison Writing Program sponsors an annual writing contest, publishes the free book Handbook for Writers In Prison, provides one-on-one mentoring to prisoners, conducts workshops, and seeks to promote prisoners' work publicly through literary publications and readings.
Pen American Center, 588 Broadway, Suite 303, New York, NY 10012